The Substance-Related Disorder Assessment

A Road Map to Effective Treatment Planning

Matthew Sprong | **Sharon Davis**
Northern Illinois University | Arkansas State University

Kendall Hunt
publishing company

Cover image © Shuterstock, Inc.

Kendall Hunt
publishing company

www.kendallhunt.com
Send all inquiries to:
4050 Westmark Drive
Dubuque, IA 52004-1840

Copyright © 2018 by Kendall Hunt Publishing Company

ISBN 978-1-5249-5975-3

Published in the United States of America

To our students, mentors, and colleagues who we learn from every day and to our families whose love, dedication, patience, and cheerleading make it all worthwhile. And to everyone whose lives have been devastated by substance use—it is for you that we dedicate our careers.

Contents

Preface

Assessment is the foundation on which treatment planning is built. A weak assessment will lead to sloppy treatment planning and, quite frankly, your clients deserve your best when it comes to their treatment plan. This text will guide counselors and counselors-in-training in how to conduct a solid and accurate assessment. Assessing clients is a huge responsibility and the task should not be taken lightly. Assessments lead to diagnoses and diagnoses stay in your client's permanent record forever. As a counselor, you will need to know when to assess and how to assess. This book will guide you in both of these. Not every client needs a substance use assessment, and so you may want to start with a screening. Screening instruments are short and easy to administer, but they do not yield adequate information from which to build a treatment plan or to determine a diagnosis. The purpose of a screening is to quickly identify those clients who would benefit from a full substance use assessment. As you read this book, you will learn the differences between screenings and assessments and you will be able to choose reliable and valid instruments for each process.

This book also describes important ethical and multicultural issues that are relevant to assessment. The 21st-century counselor must adhere to ethical codes, and we have to serve our clients from a place of cultural fairness and consideration. The practice of testing and assessment has a dark history wrought with cultural bias, discrimination, and abhorrent treatment of minorities. As counselors, we need to put our clients first. This means we follow our codes of ethics, we value cultural differences, and we always keep learning.

Assessment is part science and part art. Accurate assessing takes learning and practice. We hope you will use this book to help you on your journey, and, together, we can help improve treatment services for the clients whom we have dedicated our life's work.

Chapter 1

Introduction to Assessment
Sharon J. Davis

Key Terms: addiction, substance-related disorders, substance use disorders, substance abuse, substance dependence

Key Objectives: This chapter will provide students with an understanding of the history of drug and alcohol treatment, models of addiction, and current treatment practices for substance-related disorders.

Treatment for Alcohol and Drug Addictions

Although the "War on Drugs" has waged for several decades, drug use continues to rise in the United States. In 2015, 9.4% of individuals age 12 and over reported past month use of an illicit drug (National Institute on Drug Abuse [NIDA], 2015). Binge drinking of alcohol also remains high with 30.2% of males and 16% of females engaging in binge drinking (five or more drinks on the same occasion) during the past month (NIDA, 2015). According to national studies, there are over 22 million people in the United States in need of substance use treatment, yet only around 2.5 million actually receive it (NIDA, 2015). Substance abuse treatment as a profession has a long history and there is still much we have yet to learn. The purpose of this book is to provide counselors and counselors-in-training with a comprehensive guide for assessing substance-related and addictive disorders, but first here are some important terms for you to learn.

With the release of the *Diagnostic and Statistical Manual of Mental Disorders* (Fifth Edition; *DSM-5*) in 2013 came new terminology in the field of addictions. The previous version of the DSM described people with severe substance use disorders (SUDs) as having *substance dependence* and those with mild or moderate symptoms as having *substance abuse*. Dependence was synonymous with addiction, a term that has long been used to describe being either physiologically or psychologically enslaved to the use of drugs or alcohol. According to the *DSM-5*, a person with a pathological pattern of behaviors related to substance use is a person with a SUD. A substance-related disorder includes SUDs, substance intoxication, and substance withdrawal. For the purpose of this text, a *person with a substance use disorder* is a person who meets the *DSM-5* diagnostic criteria for a cluster of cognitive, behavioral, and physiological symptoms as a result of their continued use of drugs or alcohol. This chapter will review the history of substance use and treatment and will provide you with a foundation on which to build your assessment knowledge and skills.

History of Treatment

For thousands of years, human beings have been using substances for healing, health, happiness, and mental escape. Ancient Sumerian writings referring to opium poppies as "Joy Plant" have been found which date back 6000 years (Hanson, Venturelli, & Fleckenstein, 2009) and alcohol is discussed in several ancient texts including the Christian Bible, Muslim Quran, and the Precepts of Buddhism. Some ancient Egyptian pictographs have even featured wine and beer making. The ancient Egyptians and Greeks even had gods associated with alcohol and the Greek word, *narkoticos*, from which we get our word *narcotics*, means benumbing or deadening (Hanson et al., 2009).

For as long as humans have used substances, humans have also misused, abused, and become dependent on them. Centuries ago, people with SUDs were thrown in jail, locked up in asylums, or made social outcasts. It was not until the 20th century that the profession of substance abuse treatment formed. We have come a long way since the early days of treatment and with the help of modern science and years of research into what works and what does not, we have arrived at the most exciting time in history to be part of this profession.

It is the era of evidence-based practices, yet even with the huge advances we as a profession have made, societal attitudes for many have remained stagnate for hundreds of years, and maybe even thousands of years. Today, prisons are packed with people convicted of using illicit substances, those with drug charges on their records are turned down for employment, and communities and families have turned their backs on people for using—making them social outcasts.

People with SUD are viewed differently than people with other disorders. While much stigma still exists for many with mental health disorders like schizophrenia and bipolar disorder, it is considerably less common for people to blame those with these types of disorders for their condition. And for physical disabilities, like blindness, Parkinson's disease, Alzheimer's disease, and amyotrophic lateral sclerosis (ALS), blaming the individual is nearly unheard of. It is all too easy for others to attribute blame for SUDs on the person's low morals, lack of willpower, deficits of character, or sinful nature. This attitude permeates society and for decades was prevalent even among treatment providers. Our goal for this text is to look at SUDs from a new perspective—one that is rooted in empowerment, empathy, and a holistic approach—a *rehabilitation modeled* approach for students on their way to becoming treatment professionals.

The term "alcoholism" was first introduced in 1849 by the Swedish physician Magnus Huss (Lesch et al., 1990; Miller, Forcehimes, & Zweben, 2011). It was around this same time that the Temperance Movement in the United States began calling for widespread abstinence from alcohol. The Women's Christian Temperance Movement rallied against "demon rum," labeling it the root cause of the disintegration of families (Van Wormer & Davis, 2008). Setting the foundation for nationwide sobriety, the Temperance Movement aided in efforts for legislative action prohibiting alcohol manufacture and consumption. Prohibition lasted from 1920 to 1933. During that time, the United States saw a rise in organized crime, illegal manufacture and bootlegging of alcohol, the rise of *speakeasies*, and the criminalizing of alcohol consumers. Known as the "noble experiment," prohibition did little to curb society's appetite for alcohol (Van Wormer & Davis, 2008). With the passage of the 21st amendment, prohibition was repealed.

The use of what are now illicit drugs has long been prevalent. Cocaine, opium, heroin, and marijuana were all legal during the 19th century. Many over-the-counter concoctions, known as "patent medicines," containing opium or cocaine were hailed as effective in curing a long list of ailments including pain due to infant teething, toothaches, liver and kidney problems, and coughs. Even Coca-Cola contained cocaine and was advertised as an intellectual beverage and temperance drink (Hanson et al., 2009). By 1930, however, laws had been passed making cocaine, opium, heroin, and marijuana illegal (Capuzzi & Stauffer, 2008).

It was in 1935 that *Alcoholics Anonymous* (AA) was founded by Bill Wilson and Dr. Bob Smith (Kurtz, 1991). AA is a self-help movement based on the notion that individuals with alcohol use disorders need the support of each other and a Higher Power in order to maintain sobriety. Still widely popular, AA has swept the globe and is one of the most recognizable recovery programs available. The first professional treatment programs were established in the 1940s (Holloway, 2010). Early treatment relied heavily on the use of group therapy, the disease model, and principles of AA (Holloway, 2010).

Addiction Models

Moral Model

Over the decades, people have tried to conceptualize addiction with various models. One of the earliest models of addiction is the moral model. According to this model, addiction results from a defect in character—a moral failing. This model implies that addiction is a personal choice, and, if afflicted individuals simply tried hard enough or used willpower, they could overcome their addiction. Advocates of this model believe that SUDs are symptoms of immorality and lawlessness and should be legislated away and punished like other criminal acts. Unfortunately, the moral model has been and continues to be prevalent in society. It seems the moral model is running the "war on drugs" and despite decades of research, society continues to attempt to rehabilitate persons with SUDs through punishment and incarceration.

Disease Model

The disease model of SUDs is by no means new. Built on a research article published by E.M. Jellinek in 1947, the disease model asserts that addiction is a chronic and progressive disease influenced by biological factors which cause the user to have no control over his or her use. The disease model has been embraced by AA and numerous treatment programs for decades (Hanson et al., 2009). In 1956, the American Medical Association adopted the disease model, describing alcoholism as "a chronic illness characterized by preoccupation with alcohol and loss of control over its consumption" (Van Wormer & Davis, 2008, p. 10). Soon after, treatment agencies began to emerge all over the country and even insurance companies embraced this new model and began to cover the costs of treatment (Benshoff & Jankowski, 2000).

Biopsychosocial Model

Another popular model of addiction is the biopsychosocial model (Van Wormer & Davis, 2008). This model takes a holistic approach to the etiology and treatment of addiction by focusing on the interaction of biological, psychological, and social factors which contribute to the disorder. Over the past two decades, advances in neuroscience has allowed researchers greater understanding of the science of addiction. Newer technologies like fMRI and PET scans now enable scientists to "see" inside the brain and have allowed researchers to understand the neurological factors associated with SUDs like never before. For example, researchers have used fMRIs to see the brain exhibit craving states when exposed to certain drug cues or "relapse triggers" (Goldstein & Volkow, 2011).

In 2016, the Surgeon General released the Surgeon General's Report on Alcohol, Drugs, and Health. This was the first report of its kind and calls for nationwide prioritization of SUDs as a public health crisis. In fact, according to this report, the Surgeon General has determined that "alcohol and drug misuse, substance use disorders and addiction are the most pressing public health concerns facing America." The Surgeon General's report calls for educators, treatment providers, healthcare practitioners, advocators, policy makers, community members, families, and individuals to come together and work on establishing evidence-based programs and solutions to address the problems created by drugs and alcohol. The War on Drugs began in 1971 with a declaration by President Richard Nixon. Yet, billions of dollars later, alcohol and other drugs are still causing untold pain and suffering for people with SUDs, their families, and society. Criminalization of SUDs has not worked to solve this crisis. We need a new approach based on a new model. For too long, the moral model has led to stigmatizing and criminalizing individuals with SUDs. What other condition has received this sort of response? Do we arrest people with heart disease for eating fatty, fast food cheeseburgers? Of course not, that would be absurd. Yet hundreds of thousands of people are incarcerated for substance use. According to Dr. Nora Volkow, the Director of the National Institute on Drug Abuse, addiction is "a disease that affects both the brain and behavior" and it is a "brain disease that can be treated" (2014, p. 1). The American Society of Addiction Medicine (ASAM) defines addiction as "a primary, chronic disease of brain reward, motivation, memory, and related circuitry" (ASAM, 2011).

The science of addiction has amassed a plethora of evidence to back the notion that addiction is not a moral failing or a lack of willpower on the part of the user; rather, there are biochemical, functional, and structural changes in the brain associated with addiction. This chapter will review both the medical and psychological aspects of SUDs.

Your Brain on Drugs

SUDs are complex in nature. SUDs do not develop because of a single gene, one abnormal area of brain functioning, a lone neurotransmitter imbalance, or any one psychological or social factor. This is a multifaceted disorder resulting from a combination of biological, psychological, and environmental factors.

Biological Factors

Researchers have discovered several key areas of the brain which are involved in SUD. These include the basal ganglia, prefrontal cortex, extended amygdala, and dopamine and other neurotransmitters. We will describe each of these and their role in SUD, but first we'll begin with a brief overview of the brain and related features.

The human brain consists of billions and billions of neurons (or brain cells) and the connections between them. All human activities, including movement, thoughts, emotions, plans, problem solving, communicating, judgments, dreams, voluntary and involuntary processes alike use neurons. Neurons communicate through electric and chemical messages. Chemical messages are passed from one neuron to another through a space called the synapse. The synapse is where one end of a neuron comes close to, but without touching, the receiving end of another neuron. It's in the synapse where neurotransmitters (or brain chemicals) pass from one neuron to another. Neurotransmitters enter through specific pathways called receptor sites. The human brain consists of numerous types of neurotransmitters and their coordinating receptor sites, and nature has provided us with substances which can trigger the release of these neurotransmitters, like opioids which release endorphins, and substances like tetrahydrocannabinol (THC) which fit perfectly into cannabinoid receptors in our brain.

All drugs of abuse, including alcohol, cause the brain to release dopamine—our primary pleasure neurotransmitter. The following image helps illustrate how dopamine is passed from one neuron to another:

STRUCTURE OF A TYPICAL CHEMICAL SYNAPSE

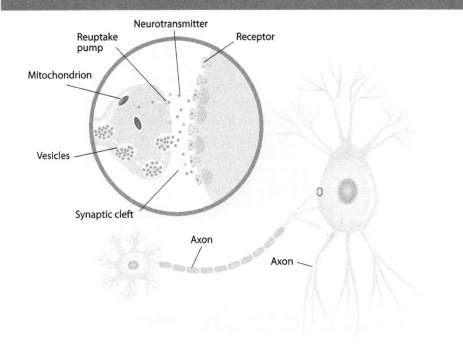

© Designua/Shutterstock.com

Nature has provided humans with a built-in reward system for engaging in activities necessary for survival, like eating food and having sex. For example, every time a human eats food, his or her brain releases dopamine which produces a pleasure feeling. That pleasurable feeling helps to ensure we want to keep eating food. It just so happens that our brains do not only reward us for doing healthy, necessary for survival activities. Our brains use the same reward system when humans use drugs or alcohol. The primary pleasure pathway in the brain lies deep within the brain in an area within the basal ganglia. The basal ganglia are also responsible for voluntary movements, cognition, emotions, and learning.

Alcohol and other drugs "hijack" this pleasure pathway in the brain and convince the brain that the substances are as important for survival as food and sex. This helps explain why individuals with SUD continue to use substances despite tragic and catastrophic consequences and why stopping is not just a matter of "willpower." The brain tells the user that they must continue to use just like our brains tell us that we must eat.

Another area of the brain at work in SUD is the extended amygdala. The amygdala is the part of the brain that controls reactions to strong emotion and the "fight or flight" response. When a person with a SUD attempts to stop taking their drug of choice, the amygdala is activated and produces a stress response, creating unpleasant feelings known as craving.

The prefrontal cortex is the area of the brain where decisions are made and consequences are weighed. In persons with SUD, the prefrontal cortex is unable to engage in adequate problem solving and impulse control, craving is allowed to take over, and the brain becomes a rogue system without guidance from the frontal lobe.

Recent research has been able to record the activity of the brain during cravings and has found that cravings occur in microseconds—faster than the brain can process images when exposed to drug cues (or relapse triggers). In other words, when a person with a SUD is exposed to a person, place, or thing that reminds them of drug use, their brain will elicit a stress response (a craving) and this happens before their prefrontal cortex is allowed to weigh in.

The Rehabilitation Model

In 2000, researchers John Benshoff and Timothy Janikowski published the Rehabilitation Model of Substance Abuse Counseling. This model conceptualizes SUD as a disability, which is "any medically diagnosable physical, cognitive, or emotional condition which is chronic or permanent in nature" (Benshoff & Janikowski, 2000, p. 17). According to this model, disabilities (including SUD) result in functional limitations and present handicaps. A functional limitation is a physical, behavioral, cognitive, or emotional limitation caused by a disability. A person who is deaf, for example, has a functional limitation in communication. Someone with a spinal cord injury resulting in complete paralysis has a functional limitation in mobility. A person with an alcohol use disorder has both physical and psychological functional limitations exacerbated or caused by alcohol. Handicaps are barriers to achieving one's goals. These include environmental obstacles (like staircases for a person with limited mobility), legislative (like laws preventing the use of emotional support animals), or attitudinal (like employer bias in hiring persons with disabilities). It is important to remember that the term handicap does not describe a person. A person may have a disability, but handicaps are obstacles which keep people from achieving life goals. A person is not handicapped. This terminology is outdated, inaccurate, and offensive. In fact, the rehabilitation model places emphasis on "person-first" terminology. For example, a person who has an alcohol use disorder is a *person with an alcohol use disorder*, not an *alcoholic*. Likewise, you would say a *person with schizophrenia* rather than a *schizophrenic*. In other words, you would say a *person with a disability*, not a disabled person. Person-first language emphasizes people may have a disorder, but they are not defined by it. The rehabilitation model stresses the importance of assisting clients in reaching their life goals. This model is built on counselor–client collaboration and client autonomy. The rehabilitation model acknowledges that there are biological, psychological, and social factors involved in the etiology of SUD, but it takes a less medical and more client-centered approach to treatment.

Models are important because they help shape our attitudes toward addictions and guide our approach to treatment. For example, a clinician who adopts a moral model approach will likely blame the client for his or her addiction and will use a confrontational therapeutic style. In contrast, the clinician who adopts a biopsychosocial or rehabilitation model will see addiction as the result of many factors and will take a multifaceted and holistic approach to therapy.

The Importance and Use of Clinical Skills

There are specific clinical skills which serve as the foundation for effective assessment and treatment. These are fundamental through each step of treatment and include empathy, collaboration, and unconditional positive regard. Empathy is the ability to deeply understand one's client. It is the capacity to "put oneself in another's shoes" and then to express this deep understanding in a nonjudgmental manner. Many counseling approaches include empathy, but it gets its start in the client-centered approach popularized by Carl Rogers. In 1959, Rogers described *accurate empathy* as a critical ingredient in promoting client growth and change. According to Miller et al. (2011, p. 49), "one of the strongest predictors of a counselor's effectiveness in treating substance use disorders is empathy." The technique involved in expressing empathy within the client-centered approach is known as *active listening*. Active listening involves listening intently to what a client has stated and reflecting the essence of that statement back to him or her. Through this approach, a client is able to express himself or herself freely without fear of judgment. The counselor adopts an attitude of "unconditional positive regard." Most importantly, this approach allows clients to explore their feelings and mental processes, gain insight into their behaviors, and work toward growth and change in a supportive atmosphere. The empathic counselor does not need to give advice, use anecdotes, self-disclose, or inundate the client with didactic material. The counselor needs only to focus fully on understanding the client in the here and now. Empathy is not a talent with which people are born; rather, it is a skill that is developed over time. Fortunately, for most counselors-in-training, empathy can be learned.

Introduction to Evidence-Based Practices

According to Miller et al. (2011), empathy is itself an *evidence-based practice*. Evidence-based practices are those approaches to treatment which have been proven effective. SAMHSA's National Registry of Evidence-based Programs and Practices (NREPP) is a valuable tool for clinicians who want to select approaches which have been rigorously tested. This online registry allows clinicians to choose an approach based on select demographics and settings. NREPP contains over 280 interventions, including motivational enhancement therapy, cognitive behavioral therapy (CBT), contingency management (CM), and community reinforcement approaches (CRAs; NREPP, 2013). It is important for counselors to choose from approaches which are evidence based. Chapter 8 of this book will describe more about the evidence-based practices mentioned in this chapter.

Client Readiness for Change

Change is an important element in addiction treatment. The *stages of change* as described by Prochaska and DiClemente's (1984) transtheoretical model, are used throughout treatment programs. The main premise of the stages of change is that individuals differ in their readiness to change and it is the clinician's responsibility to meet clients where they are rather than attempt to "force" them to change. The first of the five stages is *precontemplation*. At this stage, a client has not considered change—he or she does not recognize the need for it. Or perhaps, he or she has attempted to change in the past and failed and has given up the idea. The second stage is *contemplation*. Here, a client is considering change. He or she may be weighing the benefits vs. the cost, but has not yet made a decision. The third stage is *preparation*, where the client makes the decision to change but may not yet know how to go about it. Stage 4 is *action*. This is when the client has made a commitment to change and is taking the first steps toward it. For example, a client may throw out his or her stash of drugs and begins to actively implement a plan for change. In the fifth stage, *maintenance*, the client has made great progress toward change and is working on maintaining his or her new behaviors. Many clients refer to this as being in recovery.

It is important to note that clients may not progress through the stages of change in a linear fashion. Sometimes they will move back and forth between stages and may even cycle backward through stages (Miller et al., 2011). Moreover, there are no criteria dictating how long a client will stay in a given stage. Progression may be very fast, incredibly slow, or even nonexistent. Counselors need to recognize the stage in which their client is and be realistic in their expectations. Furthermore, counselors should celebrate any forward movement through the stages. If a client is at the precontemplation stage at the beginning of treatment and only begins preparation for change before dropping out, that client has moved two whole stages. Although this may not be the "miracle" the counselor was hoping to see, it is still change. Perhaps, the client will later return to treatment ready to begin the action stage.

Motivational interviewing is an evidence-based practice which increases a client's motivation for change and is particularly useful for clients in the contemplation and preparation stages (Emmelkamp & Vedel, 2006). When a client reaches the action stage, he or she is likely well motivated and ready for change. This is when a cognitive behavioral approach may be appropriate (Emmelkamp & Vedel, 2006). The focus of CBT is on changing irrational beliefs and unhealthy behaviors. It combines elements of

Albert Ellis' rational emotive behavior therapy (REBT) and Aaron Beck's approach to cognitive therapy (Rosenberg & Kosslyn, 2011). REBT helps clients replace irrational, destructive ways of thinking with rational ways. In REBT, the counselor takes a direct role in disputing a client's distorted beliefs. An example is a client's "must" statements, such as "I *must* get this job" or "I *must* be accepted by my family." The clinician would counter these statements by pointing out that whereas getting that job or being accepted is preferable, it is not something that must happen. The clinician may rephrase the statement like this: "It will be very unpleasant if I'm not accepted by my family, but it will not be unbearable." In Beck's cognitive therapy, the counselor focuses on the client's faulty automatic thoughts. Negative automatic thoughts can lead to unhealthy client behavior. For example, if a client thinks finding new sober friends is impossible because they will look down on him or her, then the client is likely to avoid attempts to make new friends altogether. Clients are often asked to keep daily accounts of their situations, corresponding emotions, automatic thoughts, and outcomes as "homework." In this approach, clients learn to replace automatic thoughts with rational responses (Rosenberg & Kosslyn, 2011).

CM is a CBT that has been shown to be particularly effective in treating alcohol, cocaine, and opioid dependence (Capuzzi & Stauffer, 2008). This approach uses external incentives (rewards) to reinforce client adherence to treatment goals. For example, a client may receive a gift certificate to a restaurant upon completing a certain number of clean urinalysis tests. Another cognitive behavioral approach is the CRA. CRA is based on the idea that a client's environment or community actively reinforces his or her recovery (Capuzzi & Stauffer, 2008). The focus then is on changing environmental factors so that they no longer act as "triggers" for relapse. CRA addresses vocational, social, recreational, and family issues.

Pharmacological Interventions

In recent years, medical advances and greater understanding of the neurological factors involved in addiction have led to an increase in the popularity of pharmacological interventions. Medications like disulfiram (Antabuse) and methadone are probably the most well-known pharmacological treatments. Disulfiram was the first pharmacological intervention used for alcohol addiction (Capuzzi & Stauffer, 2008). If a person drinks alcohol while taking this medication, he or she will suffer an unpleasant (and possibly life-threatening) physical reaction. It acts as a type of aversion therapy for alcohol. First synthesized in Germany in 1943, methadone helps prevent cravings and reduce withdrawal in those dependent on heroin (Hanson et al., 2009). It is the most widely used treatment of its kind (Washton & Zweben, 2006). Incidentally, methadone was originally named Dolophine, after Adolf Hitler (Hanson et al., 2009).

Newer pharmacological treatments include naltrexone for the treatment of opioid and alcohol dependence and acamprosate (Campral) and baclofen (Lioresal) to relieve alcohol withdrawal (Capuzzi & Stauffer, 2008). Buprenorphine is a promising newer medication used for opioid dependence. It helps block cravings and eases withdrawal. In 2000, the Drug Addiction Treatment Act allowed qualified and trained physicians to dispense buprenorphine to their patients more easily. Safer than methadone, buprenorphine has a very low chance of lethal overdose (Washton & Zweben, 2006). When used in conjunction with therapy, pharmacological interventions can increase a client's chances at recovery.

Types of Treatment

Detoxification

Detoxification alone does not constitute treatment (Center for Substance Abuse Treatment, 2006), but for clients suffering the effects of withdrawal, detoxification (known also as detox) is often called for. There are varying levels of care when it comes to detox. Medical detox occurs in a hospital setting and is appropriate for clients addicted to alcohol or a class of antianxiety medications known as benzodiazepines. Withdrawal from these substances can be dangerous, leading to seizures or even death. For clients at risk of dangerous withdrawal, a medical setting is the safest place for detox. Social setting detox (nonmedical detox) is often available at community-based treatment agencies. This is a lower cost option for people with non–life-threatening withdrawal. Most detox programs last only a few days, and it is important for clients to enter a treatment program immediately after detox.

Brief Intervention

Brief intervention (BI) has become an increasingly popular treatment modality which is well suited for light to moderate users or those at risk of developing a drug or alcohol problem. The goal of BI is to investigate potential problems and increase motivation to change (Center for Substance Abuse Treatment, 1999). BIs are time limited and cost effective. BI can help clients to reduce or stop their use of substances on their own and change other specific behaviors. BI also works well as a precursor to treatment (Center for Substance Abuse Treatment, 1999).

Inpatient/Residential

There are several types of inpatient/residential treatment programs. Some of these are the 28-day programs while others are more time intensive, lasting from 3 to 6 months. Studies show that longer stays in substance abuse treatment are more effective. Specifically, according to the National Institute on Drug Abuse (2012), most clients need at least 3 months in treatment to significantly reduce or stop their drug use and many clients require multiple episodes of treatment. Inpatient/residential treatment programs often incorporate individual and group therapy, as well as family therapy. Many also encourage clients to attend 12-step groups like AA. Upon completion of inpatient/residential treatment, clients will often complete an aftercare program.

Aftercare, also known as continuing care, is an important follow-up to inpatient/residential treatment. It helps clients to maintain recovery while back in their communities. Newly learned skills can be practiced and reinforced in the "real world." Aftercare may last for varying lengths of time, based on client needs.

Outpatient

Outpatient treatment is a less costly and less restrictive alternative to inpatient/residential treatment. It is well suited for clients who can maintain sobriety and change behaviors while remaining in their own environment. There are several advantages to outpatient treatment, one of which is that it is less life intrusive—clients attend school or work and take care of their home responsibilities while in treatment. Also, clients are able to practice newly learned skills in their community. Outpatient treatment frequently consists of both individual and group therapies. Many outpatient agencies are using evidence-based practices like motivational interviewing, cognitive behavioral therapies, and pharmacological interventions. Clients are often encouraged to attend 12-step meetings, while in outpatient treatment. For clients whose environments do not support recovery efforts or for those who have been unsuccessful in outpatient treatment, inpatient/residential treatment may be more appropriate.

Mandated Treatment

Many clients who enter substance abuse treatment do not do so voluntarily. According to Farabee, Prendergast, and Anglin (1998), requiring individuals to complete treatment has been ongoing since the 1920s when morphine addicts were forced into treatment. Long before the 1920s, those with alcohol dependence were forced into asylums. Detaining individuals in these asylums was thought to be necessary in order to "cure" those with alcohol dependence, known as "inebriates" in the 19th century (Brown, 1985). Currently, at least half of clients in treatment are mandated to be there (Farabee et al., 1998). Drug-related charges and driving under the influence (DUI) are common reasons for the courts to order someone to complete a treatment program. Over the years, there has been much debate over the effectiveness of mandated or coerced treatment (Burke & Gregoire, 2007; Zhang, Roberts, & Lansing, 2012). It is known that intrinsic motivation is important in order for a person to change his or her drug-using behavior in other words; the person has to *want* to change (Miller & Rollnick, 1991). And some would argue that clients mandated to treatment lack the necessary desire for change, therefore treatment cannot be effective. Other concerns over mandated treatment involve the impact of coercion on the therapeutic relationship, which is often seen as the most important predictor of successful counseling (SAMHSA, 2014). Coerced clients are often described by therapists as being hostile, resistant, and unmotivated (Miller & Rollnick, 1991). However, according to a meta-analysis by the National Institute on Drug Abuse (2014), most studies show that treatment outcomes for those required to go to treatment are as good as for voluntary admissions, and mandated clients tend to stay longer in treatment and have better attendance rates. Burke and Gregoire (2007) found that mandated clients were *more likely* to remain abstinent from drugs and alcohol 30 days after treatment than voluntary clients.

Purpose of Assessment in Substance Abuse Counseling

When a client first presents for treatment, he or she undergoes a thorough assessment. An assessment provides the clinician with an overall understanding of the client's symptoms, strengths, needs, and supports. The assessment will also include questions to determine if the client meets criteria for a diagnosis. Information gathered from the assessment is used to build a treatment plan. A good assessment is holistic. It will include information about the client's drug and alcohol use, vocational history, education, psychological, and social factors. The assessment is the foundation on which client treatment is built. From it, you will chart a plan for treatment. Good treatment starts with a good assessment. The ingredients of a good assessment include: a client-centered and holistic model, evidence-based clinical skills, and a valid and reliable instrument. The following chapters will help you in choosing the right instrument and will guide you in conducting a quality assessment.

Conclusion

Addiction treatment has a long and interesting history and not all approaches and models were effective. Recent advances in psychopharmacology and the emphasis on evidence-based practices is increasing the effectiveness of substance abuse treatment. Whether inpatient or outpatient, voluntary or mandated, treatment outcomes can be successful and people with SUDs can recover.

References

American Society of Addiction Medicine (2011). Public Policy Statement: Definition of Addiction. Retrieved from https://www.asam.org/resources/definition-of-addiction.

Brown, E. M. (1985). "What shall we do with the inebriate?" Asylum treatment and the disease concept of alcoholism in the late nineteenth century. *Journal of the History of Behavioral Science, 21*(1), 48–59.

Benshoff, J. J., & Janikowski, T. P. (2000). The Rehabilitation Model of Substance Abuse Counseling. Belmont, CA: Wadsworth.

Burke, A. C., & Gregoire, T. K. (2007). Substance abuse treatment outcomes for coerced and non-coerced clients. *Health and Social Work, 32*(1), 7–15.

Capuzzi, D., & Stauffer, M. D. (2008). *Foundations of addictions counseling.* Boston, MA: Allyn and Bacon.

Center for Substance Abuse Treatment. (1999). *Brief interventions and brief therapies for substance abuse.* Treatment Improvement Protocol (TIP) Series 34. HHS Publication No. (SMA) 09-3952. Rockville, MD: Substance Abuse and Mental Health Services Administration.

Center for Substance Abuse Treatment. (2006). *Detoxification and substance abuse treatment.* Treatment Improvement Protocol (TIP) Series 45. DHHS Publication No. (SMA) 06-4131. Rockville, MD: Substance Abuse and Mental Health Services Administration.

Emmelkamp, P. M. G., & Vedel, E. (2006). *Evidence-based treatment for alcohol and drug abuse.* New York, NY: Routledge.

Farabee, M. D., Prendergast, L., & Anglin, M. D. (1998). The effectiveness of coerced treatment for drug-abusing offenders. *Federal Probation, 62*(1), 3–10.

Goldstein R. Z., & Volkow N. D. (2011). Dysfunction of the prefrontal cortex in addiction: Neuroimaging findings and clinical implications. *Nature Reviews Neuroscience, 12,* 652–69.

Hanson, G. R., Venturelli, P. J., & Fleckenstein, A. E. (2009). *Drugs and society* (10th ed.). Sudbury, MA: Jones and Bartlett.

Holloway, L. (2010). New strategies for intervention with individuals. In A. A. Abbott (Ed.), *Alcohol, tobacco, and other drugs: Challenging the myths, assessing theories, individualizing interventions* (pp. 277–329). Washington, DC: NASW Press.

Lesch, O. M., Kefer, J., Lentner, S., Mader, R., Marz, B., Musalek, M., ... Rustembegovich, A. (1990). Diagnosis of chronic alcoholism—Classificatory problems. *Psychopathology, 23,* 88–96.

Miller, W. R., Forcehimes, A. A., & Zweben, A. (2011). *Treating addiction: A guide for professionals.* New York, NY: Guilford.

Miller, W. R., & Rollnick, S. (1991). *Motivational interviewing: Preparing people to change addictive behavior.* New York, NY: Guilford.

National Institute on Drug Abuse. (2012). Principals of drug addiction treatment: A research based guide (3rd ed.). Retrieved from http://www.drugabuse.gov/publications/principles-drug-addiction-treatment-research-based-guide-third-edition/principles-effective-treatment

National Institute on Drug Abuse. (2014). Principals of drug abuse treatment for criminal justice populations: A research based guide. Retrieved from http://drugabuse.gov/publications/principals-drug-abuse-treatment-criminal-justice-populations

National Institute on Drug Abuse. (2015). Drug facts: Nationwide trends. Retrieved from www.drugabuse.gov/publications/drugfacts/nationwide-trends

National Registry of Evidence-based Programs and Practices. (2013). Retrieved from www.nrepp.samhsa.gov

Prochaska, J. O., & DiClemente, C. C. (1984). *The transtheoretical approach: Crossing traditional boundaries of therapy.* Homewood, IL: Dow/Jones Irwin.

Rosenberg, R. S., & Kosslyn, S. M. (2011). *Abnormal psychology.* New York, NY: Worth.

Substance Abuse and Mental Health Services Administration. (2014). Evidence-based therapy relationships. Retrieved from http://www.nrepp.samhsa.gov/Norcross.aspx

Van Wormer, K., & Davis, D. R. (2008). *Addiction treatment: A strength's perspective* (2nd ed.). Belmont, CA: Brooks/Cole.

Washton, A. M., & Zweben, J. E. (2006). *Treating alcohol and drug problems in psychotherapy practice: Doing what works.* New York, NY: Guilford.

Zhang, S. X., Roberts, R. E. L., & Lansing, A. E. (2012). Treatment or else: Coerced treatment for drug-involved California parolees. *International Journal of Offender Therapy and Comparative Criminology, 57*(7), 766–791.

Chapter 2

I

Diagnostic Criteria of Substance-Related Disorders

Sharon J. Davis

Key Terms: diagnostic criteria, tolerance, withdrawal, severity, specifier

Key Objectives: This chapter will allow students to (a) understand the background of the development of the diagnostic criteria for substance use disorders; (b) be able to apply *DSM-5* diagnostic criteria for substance use disorders to case study examples.

Introduction

In 2013, the American Psychiatric Association (APA) published the 5th edition of the Diagnostic and Statistical Manual of Mental Disorders, more commonly called the *DSM-5*. It provides counselors with a complete guide for diagnosing mental health disorders, including substance use disorders (SUDs). This chapter will provide counselors with a thorough overview of the history, features, and techniques associated with substance use diagnostics and the DSM.

Historical Background

The Disease Model

As you will recall from Chapter 1, for thousands of years, humans have been seeking out plants, herbs, and other concoctions to treat ailments, relieve stress, increase health and longevity, enhance mood, and to get high and as long as humans have been using these substances, humans have also been struggling with the consequence of their use. For centuries, SUDs were thought of as defect of character or a moral failing. The moral model has led to misunderstanding and stigma of those with SUDs throughout history. And, even treatment professionals have followed the moral model in the past, leading to mistreatment of individuals with SUD. However, in the early 19th century, Dr. Benjamin Rush (1745–1813), the Father of American Psychiatry, became the first to describe addiction as a brain disease. Rush wrote the first psychiatric textbook in the United States in 1812 (Penn Medicine, 2017).

In 1947, scientist E. M. Jellinek developed the *disease concept* of alcoholism. Jellinek proposed that certain individuals have a biological sensitivity or "allergy" to alcohol, and, if they consume alcohol, they risk developing the disease of alcoholism. He outlined the path to alcoholism as follows (cited in Benshoff & Janikowski, 2000):

Normal drinking>> heavy/frequent drinking>>drunken bouts/secret drinking/morning drinking>>blackouts/tolerance/withdrawal>>loss of control over drinking>>slavery to alcohol/death

The Disease Model, as it came to be known, describes alcoholism as progressive in nature and irreversible. Perhaps you have heard the saying "once an alcoholic, always an alcoholic?" This philosophy has been controversial over the years. Many people have struggled with the idea of a person being sober for years and years still having the label of an "alcoholic." Some would say the idea of a person being powerless over alcohol is a rather hopeless view and can even create an excuse for relapse. Also, critics point to flaws in Jellinek's original data from which he based his theory. His sample size consisted of less than 100 people and no women were included (Capuzzi & Stauffer, 2008). Furthermore, the path to alcoholism as described by Jellinek is not always as predictable as he postulated. To his credit, Jellinek did lay the groundwork for understanding the science behind addiction and helped us move away from the stigmatizing and archaic moral model. Jellinek's disease model was later generalized to include drugs other than alcohol.

The 1940s brought exciting growth to the understanding of addiction from a scientific perspective. Just a few years earlier, Bill Wilson and Bob Smith founded the self-help group *Alcoholics Anonymous* (AA). And by 1939, the first publication of the "Big Book," *Alcoholics Anonymous*, was published. In 1944, Marty Mann, one of the first women to achieve recovery through participation in AA, started the National Committee for Education on Alcoholism (NCEA), which is now known as the National Council on Alcoholism and Drug Dependence (NCADD, 2015). The NCADD is the leading advocacy organization for SUDs. Mann knew that for the NCADD to have a real impact in changing people's attitude and understanding of alcoholism, it had to have the involvement and support of the scientific community. Sadly, Mann has often been overlooked in the history of addiction, yet it is her clear understanding of the significance of including the scientific community that was, perhaps, one of the most important contributions to the treatment of SUD.

The NCADD was one of the first organizations to earnestly arouse public interest in alcoholism and pioneered public educational campaigns based on the science of addiction. Other important contributions of the NCADD include:

1. Engaging the medical profession in the approach of addiction as a brain disease rather than a moral failing.
2. Establishing the foundation for the development of the first Employee Assistance Programs (EAPs), which provide help to workers facing alcohol and drug problems in companies across the nation.
3. Establishing addictions teaching programs for professionals and providing national resources for educational materials on addictions.
4. Developing the first medical criteria for the diagnosis of alcoholism.
5. Advocating successfully for insurance companies to cover the costs of treatment for SUD.

It was also because of the work of the NCADD that in 1956, the American Medical Association defined alcoholism as a primary and chronic disease that is both progressive and fatal. A *primary* disease is one that occurs on its own and is not simply the symptom of another condition. For example, diabetes is a primary disease which can occur on its own, but diabetes can result in blindness. Blindness caused by diabetes would be considered a secondary disease resulting from a primary disease. The term *chronic* means it is incurable and will remain lifelong, and even if a person experiences remission, relapse is still likely (Benshoff & Janikowski, 2000).

With the American Medical Association accepting alcoholism as a brain disease, advances in research and treatment grew exponentially across the nation. The profession of substance abuse counseling formed and treatment protocols began to emerge. By the 1950s, the treatment community was embracing the disease model of addiction. Yet the 1952 publication of the first edition of the Diagnostic and Statistical Manual for Mental Disorders proved that much work still needed to be done and the moral model was still alive and well.

The Diagnostic and Statistical Manual (DSM)

In 1952, the APA published its first edition of the DSM (Kawa & Giordano, 2012). This early predecessor included 102 disorders and was based largely on a psychodynamic approach to psychological disorders. The first DSM used the term *alcoholism* and defined it as having an "alcohol addiction." It did not provide any specific criteria, however. Both alcoholism and drug dependence were considered a subset of sociopathic personality disorders along with antisocial personality disorder, sexual deviations, and homosexuality (Roget & Fischer, 2009). Moreover, this earliest version of the DSM described alcoholism and drug dependence from a moral model approach in which the person continues using because of a lack of willpower and a defect of character. Sadly, the classification and definitions of alcoholism and drug dependence remained virtually unchanged in the DSM until its third revision in 1980. The *DSM-III* introduced the term "substance use disorders" and reclassified them as their own category. Also, the *DSM-III* was the first to differentiate between substance abuse and substance dependence. *Substance abuse* was defined as "a pattern of pathological use, impairment in social or occupational functioning due to substance use, and minimal duration of disturbance of at least one month" (APA, 1980, p. 163). *Substance dependence*, on the other hand, was defined as a more severe form of substance use which included "tolerance or withdrawal" (APA, 1980, p. 163). Five classes of substances were described in terms of both substance abuse and dependence in the *DSM-III*. These were alcohol, barbiturates or similarly acting sedative/hypnotics, opioids, amphetamines, and cannabis. Phencyclidine (PCP), cocaine, and hallucinogens were only associated with substance abuse because of a lack of evidence for physiological dependence (APA, 1980).

Over 60 years since the first edition, the *DSM-5* is considered *the* reference for diagnostic criteria of psychological disorders in the United States. The *DSM-5* is far more reliable and valid than its earlier editions. It took hundreds of experts over 12 years to complete this newest revision. Evidence for the *DSM-5* comes from advancements in neuroscience, genetics, brain imaging, and epidemiology (APA, 2013). As a counselor, you will want training and experience in using the *DSM-5* to diagnose SUDs in your clients.

Substance-Related Disorders

New terminology, along with an innovative conceptualization of SUDs, sets the *DSM-5* apart from its predecessors. The binary diagnoses of substance abuse and substance dependence were done away with in favor of a spectrum approach (Fetting, 2016) and after years of research, gambling disorder was finally included as an "addictive disorder" (APA, 2013) rather than an impulse control disorder.

Using the *DSM-5*

Substance-related disorders in the *DSM-5* comprise 10 classes of drugs. These drugs are alcohol, caffeine, cannabis, hallucinogens, inhalants, opioids, sedative/hypnotic/anxiolytics, stimulants, tobacco, and other. There are two groups of substance-related disorders: SUDs and substance-induced disorders. SUD is the accepted terminology for what were previously known as substance abuse and dependence. And substance-induced disorders include intoxication, withdrawal, and other substance/medication-induced medical disorders.

When a person continues to use one or more classes of drugs despite having cognitive, behavioral, or physiological symptoms due to their use, the person may be considered to have a SUD. Use of all 10 classes of drugs, except caffeine, can result in a SUD. The *DSM-5* describes SUD as a pathological "pattern of use" and it divides criteria or symptoms into overall groupings of behaviors. These groupings are based on impaired control, social impairment, risky use, and pharmacological criteria. A person has *impaired control* when he or she seems to lack control over how much or how long he or she uses a substance. Specific criteria (or symptoms) reflecting impaired control include the following:

1. Taking a substance in larger amounts or over a longer period than intended;
2. There is a persistent desire or unsuccessful efforts to cut down or control use;
3. A great deal of time is spent in activities necessary to obtain the substance, use the substance, or recover from its effect;
4. Craving, or a strong desire or urge to use the substance.

For example, a client tells you that he or she planned on limiting their cocaine use to one line at a party last Friday night, but ended up doing several lines or a client tells you that he or she has tried to stop smoking cigarettes several times, but has not been able to quit. Another example could be a client who spends several hours every day trying to get enough money to buy heroin. Criterion A consists of the first four of 11 criteria. The criteria can be applied to each class of drug, except caffeine. The next grouping reflects *social impairment*. These criteria are

5. Recurrent use resulting in a failure to fulfill major role obligations at work, school, or home;
6. Continued use despite having persistent or recurrent social or interpersonal problems caused or exacerbated by the effects of the substance;
7. Important social, occupational, or recreational activities are given up or reduced because of use.

Criteria 5–7 reflect substance use behaviors which cause *social impairment*. In other words, a person continues to use his or her drug of choice despite having significant substance-related problems at home, work, school, or in social settings. As an example, a client tells you that he or she dropped out of school (criterion 5), lost his or her best friend (criterion 6), or gave up his or her favorite hobby (criterion 7) because of marijuana use.

The next grouping of criteria involves *risky use* of substances. The criteria in this group include:

8. Recurrent use in situations in which it is physically hazardous;
9. Use is continued despite knowledge of having a persistent or recurrent physical or psychological problem that is likely to have been caused or exacerbated by the substance.

For example, a client would meet criterion 8 if he or she drove under the influence or while using heavy machinery on more than one occasion during the same 12-month period. And a client would meet criterion 9 if he or she continued drinking despite being told by a physician that he or she had liver disease.

The last grouping involves physiological criteria, specifically tolerance and withdrawal. These are defined as

10. Tolerance, as defined by either of the following:
    a. A need for markedly increased amounts of the substance to achieve intoxication or the desired effect
    b. A markedly diminished effect with continued use of the same amount of the substance
11. Withdrawal, as manifested by either of the following:
    a. The characteristic withdrawal syndrome for the substance
    b. The substance (or a closely related one) is taken to relieve or avoid withdrawal symptoms.

As an example, your client tells you that he or she used to feel drunk after just six beers, but now it takes at least 12 beers (criterion 10) or your client tells you when he or she is not able to use the opioid drug OxyContin, he or she experiences nausea, muscle aches, runny nose (rhinorrhea), watery eyes (lacrimation), and sweating (criterion 11). Every class of drug that produces withdrawal has specific withdrawal symptoms included in the *DSM-5*. Withdrawal symptoms have not been observed for hallucinogens or inhalants, therefore criterion 11 is not included for hallucinogen use disorder or inhalant use disorder.

Severity and Specifiers

When diagnosing a SUD, a counselor is also to identify the level of severity of the disorder and certain specifiers. The *DSM-5* uses a severity range of mild, moderate, or severe. A client with two to three criteria for any one substance during the same 12-month period would be considered to have a *mild* SUD, four to five criteria for any one substance during the same 12-month period would qualify as *moderate* SUD, and six or more criteria would be considered a *severe* SUD. Moderate is what was previously referred to as *substance abuse* in the DSM-IV-TR and severe was once called *substance dependence* (APA, 2000). A specifier is used to identify if a client is in some level or type of remission. Specifiers include: in early remission, in sustained remission, on maintenance therapy, or in a controlled environment. Early remission should be specified if the client previously meeting the criteria for diagnosis of SUD has not experienced those symptoms for at least 3 months but less than 12 months. If a person diagnosed with SUD goes more than 12 months with no symptoms, he or she is said to be in sustained remission. If a client is taking a medication to help with his or her recovery (e.g., methadone for heroin use) the counselor should add the specifier "on maintenance therapy" after the diagnosis. Also, if a client is in an environment where he or she does not have access to substances (like jail or an inpatient treatment facility), the counselor should use the specifier "in a controlled environment." Here is an example of how a counselor should phrase a client diagnosis:

303.90(F10.20) Severe Alcohol Use Disorder in early remission

The first set of numbers (303.90) is the *DSM-5* code for either moderate or severe alcohol use disorder. The *DSM-5* has a separate code for every SUD and its severity level(s). The number in the parenthesis (F10.20) is the International Classification of Disorders (ICD) designation for each specific disorder. The *DSM-5* is unique in its harmonization with the World Health Organization's (WHO) ICD system (APA, 2013).

If your client has two to three symptoms of marijuana use disorder but has been in jail the last 30 days, his or her diagnosis would be: 305.20 (F12.10) Mild Cannabis Use Disorder in a controlled environment. When diagnosing a client with a disorder based on the use of a specific substance within a class of drugs, you would identify the name of the drug. For example, use 304.40 (F15.20) Severe Methamphetamine Use Disorder if your client has a stimulant use disorder related to methamphetamine use.

Case Study 1

Sami is a 25-year-old, Caucasian female. She is referred to you for counseling by the court following a second DUI charge. Sami tells you she first used alcohol at age 13 with her friends. She stated from the time she was 13 to around 17 she drank primarily on the weekends at parties. When she was 18 she started college and her drinking increased from only a couple times a week to three to four times per week. She says that's when her drinking first got "out of control" and she lost her scholarship and got kicked out of school. After that, she got a job at a convenience store and moved back home with her parents. Sami tells you she tried to "straighten up" for a while and was sober for a year after moving back home. At age 20, she says she began drinking again, only "casually at first" but then she started to increase to more regular use, at least three to four times per week, and she typically ended up drinking until she passed out. She says this pattern lasted until she was 23 and she got her first DUI. After her first DUI, she says she became very depressed and had a lot of financial problems due to fines, legal fees, and "spending too much money." She also began arguing with her parents and they told her to move out. She says "that's when things really got bad." She tells you she moved in with a friend and they would drink and party "all the time." She said she was fired from several jobs because she was hungover and didn't show up. She also wrecked her roommate's car, but couldn't report it because she was drunk at the time of the accident. She says "I have driven drunk so many times, it's a wonder I haven't died." Sami tells you the last couple years have been kind of a blur, but now with her second DUI she is ready to make a change.

The case of Sami illustrates several diagnostic criteria. As a counselor, you will ask questions and listen for client statements which will help you identify symptoms. Clients do not typically use the same jargon as the *DSM-5*, so it will be up to you to carefully assess what they tell you. Sami's case shows a clear pattern of impairment and consequences due to alcohol use. Let's compare the diagnostic criteria for alcohol use disorder with what you know about Sami.

According to the *DSM-5*, the diagnostic criteria for Alcohol Use Disorder (APA, 2013, pp. 490–491) are:

A. A problematic pattern of alcohol use leading to clinically significant impairment or distress, as manifested by at least two of the following, occurring within a 12-month period:

1. Alcohol is often taken in larger amounts or over a longer period than was intended.
2. There is a persistent desire or unsuccessful efforts to cut down or control alcohol use.
3. A great deal of time is spent in activities necessary to obtain alcohol, use alcohol, or recover from its effects.
4. Craving, or a strong desire or urge to use alcohol.
5. Recurrent alcohol use resulting in a failure to fulfill major role obligations at work, school, or home.
6. Continued alcohol use despite having persistent or recurrent social or interpersonal problems caused or exacerbated by the effects of alcohol.
7. Important social, occupational, or recreational activities are given up or reduced because of alcohol use.
8. Recurrent alcohol use in situations in which it is physically hazardous.
9. Alcohol use is continued despite knowledge of having a persistent or recurrent physical or psychological problem that is likely to have been caused or exacerbated by alcohol.
10. Tolerance, as defined by either of the following:
    a. A need for markedly increased amounts of alcohol to achieve intoxication or desired effect.
    b. A markedly diminished effect with continued use of the same amount of alcohol.
11. Withdrawal, as manifested by either of the following:
    a. The characteristic withdrawal syndrome for alcohol (refer to criterion A and B of the criteria set for alcohol withdrawal, *DSM-5* pp. 499–500).
    b. Alcohol (or a closely related substance, such as a benzodiazepine) is taken to relieve or avoid withdrawal symptoms.

To accurately diagnose Sami you, the counselor, would identify symptoms from the information you have gathered about Sami. Diagnosing must be done with care. It is a huge responsibility for only the trained counselor. Any diagnosis made by you will be recorded in the client's permanent record. Always remember—a diagnosis never disappears!

Let's take the diagnostic criteria from the top. Note you are looking for a pattern of use leading to significant impairment or distress within any 12-month period. The first criterion involves increasing drinking in either amount and/or time. Sami told you *when she was 18 she started college and her drinking increased from only a couple times a week to three to four times per week.* And also a*t age 20 she says she began drinking again, only "casually at first" but then she started to increase to more regular use, at least three to four times per week,* This indicates twice that an increase in her drinking occurred during the same 12-month period. She would, therefore, meet the first criterion.

The second criterion looks for a pattern of being unsuccessful in attempts to quit or cut down. Sami told you about having been sober after being kicked out of college, but this is the only time she describes an attempt at sobriety. She does not meet criterion 2 because there is no pattern of trying to quit.

Criterion 3 is met when a client has devoted a lot of time to using, recovering from, or trying to obtain alcohol. Sami told you *she moved in with a friend and they would drink and party "all the time."* Notice she also stated that pattern had lasted for the past 2 years. Sami meets criterion 3.

Sami did not report to you any cravings or urges to use alcohol and so she does not meet criterion 4. Be careful not to assume she has had cravings simply because of meeting other criteria. Assumptions can lead to misdiagnosis.

Sami does report missing work repeatedly because of being hungover; therefore, she does meet criterion 5. She may also meet criterion 6 because of the arguing between her parents and her. However, it would be important to uncover if the arguing was related in any way to Sami's alcohol use.

Criterion 7 is also met by Sami because of her losing jobs repeatedly due to alcohol and criterion 8 is met because Sami told you *"I have driven drunk so many times, it's a wonder I haven't died."* Drinking while driving certainly qualifies as use in a situation in which it is physically hazardous.

From the information you have gathered from Sami it is difficult to determine if she meets criterion 9 (continued use despite physical or psychological problems associated with it). She did report having feelings of depression, but it is not clear that this was related to or exacerbated by alcohol. Always err on the safe side and remember to avoid assumptions. With the information you have, Sami does not meet criterion 9. Sami also does not report any symptoms of tolerance (criterion 10) or withdrawal (criterion 11).

Now you have determined that Sami does meet at least five of the criteria for alcohol use disorder (1, 3, 5, 7, and 8). It only takes two during any 12-month period for this diagnosis. Sami does report at least two of these occurring in the same 12-month period. She meets criteria for alcohol use disorder. Remember, however, you must also include a severity level and any specifiers. According to the diagnostic criteria, four to five symptoms fall into the moderate level of severity. She does not report any sustained amount of recovery during either the last 3 or 12 months, so her diagnosis does not require a remission specifier and Sami does not report taking any medication to manage her alcohol use nor is she in a controlled environment, therefore, no specifier is needed. Her diagnostic code based on what you currently know is: **303.90 (F10.20): moderate alcohol use disorder.**

In the following chapters of this text, you will learn about how to conduct a proper assessment, and you will be introduced to specific screening and assessment instruments. The *DSM-5* is the accepted guide on diagnostic criteria; however, as a counselor, it will be your responsibility to choose the right instrument. Moreover, only you can ensure that you have the appropriate training, competencies, and skills to provide your clients with an accurate and fair assessment.

Case Study 2

Mark, a 44-year-old African American male client has been told by his wife to seek help for his "smoking problem" or she will seek a divorce. He tells you he has been smoking marijuana since he was 20 years old. He and his wife, Tracy, have been married for 12 years and they have two children together, Elsie age 10 and Leon age 7. Mark works as a store manager for a large cell phone company and Tracy has a part-time job for a retail store. Mark tells you he has smoked daily for the past 3 years. He tells you

"I used to only use about a joint a day, but for the last year and half or so I usually smoke more." He reports during a typical day he will smoke one or two joints and a bowl. He says when he first married Tracy he only smoked "once in a while." He also reports having tried cocaine "once or twice" when he was in his early twenties and he drinks the occasional beer when he watches football games on the weekends. He denies ever drinking more than two to three 12 oz. cans of beer per occasion. He gets tearful when he talks about the possibility of Tracy leaving him, "she and my kids are my world and I wouldn't even want to live without them." Mark says Tracy has really been "on his case" about his marijuana use since he started using daily. "I just feel so stressed by the time I get off work—it's tiring, you know. I hate my job, my boss. . .I just gotta unwind when I can." Mark tells you he would love to get a different job, but since most places do drug testing he doubts he could be hired. You ask Mark if Tracy could sit in on the interview and he agrees. Tracy tells you that Mark has not been himself for the year, stating "he just seems so distracted, far away. He ignores the kids, barely talks to me, and just sits zoned out all evening. It's like he isn't even here anymore." Mark agrees he often gets in his own world when he's home. He says he just feels so drained and purposeless. He says marijuana distracts him for a little while, but when it wears off he just feels even worse. "I know I have to quit, but then what will I do? Weed's the thing that keeps me going." Mark denies having withdrawal symptoms, but admits he hasn't really gone without marijuana long enough to know how he would feel.

Which of the 11 diagnostic criteria does Mark meet?

What is his severity level?

What, if any, specifiers would apply to his diagnosis?

What is Mark's diagnostic code?

Case Study 3

Brenda is a 54-year-old, Caucasian female. She has been referred to you by her parole officer for a substance use assessment. Brenda was released from federal prison after serving 24 months for possession of methamphetamine and intent to deliver. Brenda tells you she used to use methamphetamine, but those days are behind her. "I never, ever want to go back to prison. I'm gonna get a job, stay clean, and mind my own business." Brenda reports a long history of substance use. She says when she was 15 she started sneaking alcohol from her dad's liquor cabinet and smoking cigarettes. She said alcohol was never really her thing, and, after she was 21, she really didn't drink. "I know it sounds weird, but I just never really liked the taste." When she was 22 Brenda started using cocaine. "Now, cocaine was awesome! It gave me energy. Made me feel great." She admits to using cocaine once every couple weeks during her 20s and then four to five times a week in her 30s. "When I was younger, I couldn't afford to use it much, but then the money started rolling in, and I could afford it." Brenda reports she waited tables from the time she was 13, but during her early 30s she started dealing drugs for money. "Pot, mostly, at first, but then I moved into the big time with meth." She denies any significant history of marijuana use. "I tried it once, but it didn't do it for me." Brenda tells you when she was 37 she got arrested for possession of marijuana. "I got busted with a bunch of weed, and I went to jail." She reports she served 12 months. At age 39, Brenda started using methamphetamine. She reports daily use up until the time she went to federal prison. She tells you without methamphetamine she wouldn't be able to function. "I'd just crash. . .I'd be shaking all over, all I'd want to do was sleep. . .and I'd get so depressed I couldn't stand it. By the end, it didn't matter what I had to do to get meth."

Using the information in the case study, what substances does Brenda have a history using?

Identify the criteria, severity level, specifiers, and diagnostic code(s) which apply to this client.

Summary/Conclusion

The APA has been the source for diagnostic criteria for disorders, including substance-related disorders for decades. Currently in its 5th edition, the *DSM-5* provides counselors with the most up-to-date information for making an accurate diagnosis of a SUD. Counselors can match client assessment data to determine if they meet specific diagnoses and to what severity level. The *DSM-5* provides counselors with relevant and valid information to guide them in making accurate client assessments.

References

American Psychiatric Association. (1980). *Diagnostic and statistical manual of mental disorders* (3rd ed.). Washington, DC: American Psychiatric Association.

American Psychiatric Association. (2000). *Diagnostic and statistical manual of mental disorders* (4th ed.). Washington, DC: American Psychiatric Association.

American Psychiatric Association. (2013). *Diagnostic and statistical manual of mental disorders* (5th ed.). Washington, DC: American Psychiatric Association.

Benshoff, J., & Janikowski, T. (2000). *The rehabilitation model of substance abuse counseling.* Belmont, CA: Wadsworth.

Capuzzi, D., & Stauffer, M. D. (2008). *Foundations of addictions counseling.* Boston, MA: Pearson Education.

Fetting, M. (2016). *Perspectives on substance use, disorders and addiction: With clinical cases* (2nd ed.). Los Angeles, CA: SAGE Publications, Inc.

Kawa, S., & Giordano, J. (2012). A brief historicity of the *Diagnostic and Statistical Manual of Mental Disorders*: Issues and implications for the future of psychiatric canon and practice. *Philosophy, Ethics, and Humanities in Medicine: PEHM*, 7(2). doi:10.1186/1747-5341-7-2.

National Council on Alcoholism and Drug Dependence. (2015). *Our history*. Retrieved from https://www.ncadd.org/

Penn Medicine. (2017). *History of Pennsylvania Hospital: Dr. Benjamin Rush*. Retrieved from http://www.uphs.upenn.edu/paharc/timeline/1751/tline7.html

Roget, G. L., & Fischer, N. A. (2009). Encyclopedia of Substance Abuse Prevention, Treatment and Recovery. Thousand Oaks, CA: Sage Publishing.

Chapter 3

Foundations of Standardized Assessment

Matthew E. Sprong
Noel A. Ysasi

Key Terms: psychometric properties, reliability, validity, descriptive statistics, substance abuse assessment

Key Objectives: Students should be better prepared to identify and gather needed client assessment data, and interpret assessment information and use it in substance abuse treatment planning.

Introduction and the Nature of Tests

Assessment is a crucial factor in the treatment of individuals who have drug and alcohol challenges. Often times, individuals requiring treatment have several barriers that may decrease the likelihood of having a perceived high quality of life. Such barriers may include loss of employment, difficulty maintaining healthy relationships, and legal challenges. Counseling professionals are tasked with identifying these barriers for several reasons, including the proper placement of the individual in the appropriate level of care (see Chapter 7), and appropriate counseling and behavioral interventions can be included (see Chapter 8) in the development of the treatment plan (see Chapter 10). Although these topics are of important interest for a counseling professional, the current chapter will focus on standardized assessment. In Chapter 2, diagnostic criteria of substance-related disorders were discussed. Often times, instruments are developed to assist in this diagnostic process. However, it is important to identify valid and reliable instruments to aid in this process. If invalid and unreliable testing occurs, the client and counseling professional may be unable to make informed decisions related to treatment.

Methods and Sources of Assessment Information

Assessment is a systematic procedure for collecting information that is used to make inferences and decisions about an individual and involves several data collection methods from multiple sources to yield relevant, accurate, and reliable information (Drummond & Jones, 2010). There are several methods to obtain information from the individual with the drug and/or alcohol barrier, such as an interview, direct observation and reviewing collateral data, and psychological testing. A comprehensive interview allows for the counseling professional to gather a great amount of information in a short period of time. Gathering information related to a person's hobbies, employment, and personal relationships are some examples of information that can be used during counseling treatment. Additionally, an interview will assist a counseling professional in understanding the individual's current situation.

Contributed by Noel A. Ysasi. © Kendall Hunt Publishing Company.

Clinical observation is one method where counseling professionals can obtain valuable information related to the client's current level of functioning (e.g., interaction with others, mood patterns), observe behaviors from clients that are used in order to determine a diagnosis, and assist in the treatment plan development. Furthermore, clinical observations are the basis of therapy and treatment and are a means by which a counseling professional can learn about his or her client (Sommers-Flanagan & Sommers-Flanagan, 2017). A counseling professional is also able to obtain collateral information from people associated with the client, such as family members, friends, medical professionals, previous treatment records (if available), and significant others. The benefit of direct observation and reviewing collateral information is that a counseling professional can compare information from what he or she is observing to determine whether the individual is making progress and completing short- and long-term goals, or if the client is not making progress. The information briefly described above (i.e., interview, direct observation, reviewing collateral information) is essential in the treatment plan development. However, the purpose of the current chapter is a focus on testing, while discussing the process of developing a test. By the end of the chapter, counseling professionals or future counseling professionals should be able to review a test and evaluate the feasibility of using that test within clinical practice.

Psychological Testing

Psychological testing is a valuable approach toward assisting a counseling professional in (a) properly diagnosing the individual, (b) determining other psychosocial limitations, and (c) evaluating the appropriate level of care for the individual in need of drug/alcohol treatment. A test is defined as an objective and standardized measure of a sample of behavior (Trochim, Donnelly, & Arora, 2014) and provides a sample of behavior that is used to predict how a person will behave in other situations of interest. A test has two primary functions, including (1) diagnosis or an estimate of a person's current status (behavior) and (2) prognosis or a prediction of a person's future status (behavior). To properly diagnose and create a prognosis of a person's future status, there are several factors to consider when selecting an instrument to use. An important factor is whether the test is standardized or implies uniformity of procedure (rules) for administration, scoring, and interpretation; and makes it possible to compare scores of different people because they have been exposed to the same stimuli. In Chapter 2, several different criteria were provided in terms of diagnosing an individual with a substance-related disorder. Although a counseling professional may be able to read the criteria and determine beyond a reasonable degree of certainty whether the individual meets the diagnosis for a mental health disorder, some instruments provide the counseling professional the ability to determine whether the behavior falls above or below an average range. Therefore, when selecting standardized assessments, the counseling professional should evaluate the test manual (all credible tests/instruments should have one) and determine if the following eight categories are discussed (Drummond & Jones, 2010):

1. Uniform test materials
2. Time limits
3. Exact oral instructions
4. Preliminary demonstrations or items, examples of which are provided
5. How to handle questions that arise from participants
6. Details of test environments
7. Norms for comparing test performance
8. Guidelines for test performance interpretation

These aforementioned categories are essential to selecting a test that will provide accurate information that can be used in treatment planning. If these features are not provided, a counseling professional

Table 1 National Certification Addiction Counselor Levels

Level of Credential	Educational Requirements	Work Experience
Level 1 (NCAC I)	GED, high school diploma, or higher	Three years' work experience or 6,000 hours supervised experience
Level 2 (NCAC II)	Bachelor's degree or higher in Substance Use Disorder/Addiction and/or related counseling subject	At least 5 years full-time experience or 10,000 hours of supervised experience
Master Addiction Counselor	Master's degree or higher in Substance Use Disorder and/or related counseling subject	At least 3 years full-time or 6,000 hours of supervised experience as a Substance Use Disorder/Addiction counselor

Adapted from "The National Certification Commission for Addiction Professionals."

may administer the test in an inappropriate manner, and the results of the test may not be objective and may provide inaccurate results. For a test to be objective, it must first avoid any subjective bias of the examiner. Specifically, the individual providing the assessment should refrain from increasing or decreasing the scoring of the test based off personal and/or professional biases. For example, teachers within a public school system often discuss with school psychologists the behavioral issues among their students. If a teacher provides the licensed specialist in school psychology (LSSP) their informal diagnosis of the student (i.e., attention deficit disorder; ADD), the LSSP can inadvertently look for behavioral signs for this particular mental health disorder and thus diagnose them with ADD. Second, the creation of test items is determined by empirical data, and test items are only administered after they have been assessed for reliability and validity.

For example, the National Certification Commission for Addiction Professionals (NCCAP) offers a standardized certification examination for individuals desiring to demonstrate they meet the minimum competencies necessary to work with clients with substance use disorder/addiction. The purpose of this credential is to standardize the quality of addiction prevention, intervention, treatment, and continuing care services (NCCAP). The certification provides three levels of credentialing which are outlined in Table 1.

Despite the requirements for sitting for an examination, each test taker should receive a subjective and reliable test which measures knowledge directly related to the area of specialty, and test conditions should be consistent for all.

Scenario 1

Suppose two individuals (Mandy from Illinois and Roger from Wisconsin) are both registered to sit for the NCCAP level-2 certification examination. When Mandy registers for the examination online, she receives no information regarding accommodations, test environment, and policies/procedures. After arriving at the testing site, the test administrator provides a hardcopy of the examination whereby Mandy must circle the correct answer choice and write out the answers for each essay question. Mandy is given a time limit of 1.5 hours. Roger, on the other hand, registers online and is provided with test site information which includes basic requirements for requesting accommodations, time limit for examinations, is ensured a noise-reduced environment, and will be provided with an electronic test format.

Once Mandy and Roger complete the examination, both are notified within 2 weeks whether they will pass the test. As the reviewers for the examination are scoring the test, they come across the essay questions and score them differently despite the answer choices for both Mandy and Roger being nearly identical.

As is noticeable from the aforementioned hypothetical scenario, the test administration was not uniform (both Mandy and Roger received different test formats), the time limit was different (while both were given 1.5 hours, Mandy had to write out her answer choices which requires more time), details of the test environment were only provided to Roger, and reviewers were not provided with how to interpret the essay questions. in line with the categories required. In order to ensure the examination is credible, the eight categories must be established. In addition to determining a test has a standardized procedure established, it is essential for a counseling professional to understand scale development and statistical concepts, reliability and validity of tests, and how to interpret the results of these types of tests.

Scale Development and Statistical Concepts

Aside from evaluating an instrument for uniformity of test administration, additional concepts counseling professionals should become familiar with prior to selecting a test to use in practice consist of the following: (a) understanding types of sampling, (b) validity, (c) reliability, (d) statistical concepts, (e) standardization process, (f) understanding assessment scores, and (g) how to interpret assessment results. A counseling professional familiar with each of these concepts will likely have a better arsenal when selecting the best test to use in clinical practice. As is likely discussed in other classes associated with training future counseling professionals, there is limited time available to meet with clients and it is essential to gather as much information in as little time as possible. Therefore, the selection of a test that can gather large amounts of information is important. However, if the test lacks "essential ingredients," the results may not be accurate.

Sampling

Suppose a researcher was interested in conducting a study where you survey individuals on their honest opinion toward the President of the United States. If the researcher surveys all of the residents in a metropolitan area that is known to be Republican, and the President is Republican, the results are likely to be skewed in favor of the President. Although it is nearly impossible to survey every person in the population to receive a generalizable result which reflects the viewpoints of most, there are ways in which researchers can obtain reliable results by selecting a subset of the population. When surveying a sample of individuals within a population, this is called sampling.

Probability Sampling. There are two types of *sampling* in research, including probability sampling and nonprobability sampling (Fitzpatrick, Sanders, & Worthen, 2011). **Probability sampling** is the process of utilizing some form of random selection of participants from the population of interest. For example, if there are 100 students in an introduction to drugs and alcohol course, a researcher may randomly select a specific number of students (e.g., 20 out of 100) from the class for a study (simple random sampling). In theory, this sample of the population will be representative of the entire student body associated with that program, because each student had an equal chance of being selected. There are several other types of probability sampling other than simple random sampling, including but not limited to:

1. *Stratified Random Sampling*: dividing the population into homogeneous subgroups and then taking a simple random sample in each subgroup.
2. *Systematic Random Sampling*: after determining the sample size desired, all of the students in the introduction to drugs and alcohol course are assigned a number (we will say there are 100 students in the course, and our desired sample size is 25 students). We would then divide the population (100 students) by our desired sample size (25 students), which would equal the number 4. We

would randomly select a number between 1 and 4. If we chose the number 3, we would then select every third student to participate in the study (e.g., 3, 6, 9, etc.).

3. ***Cluster Sampling:*** Although both stratified and systemic random sampling provide an accurate picture of the population, they both have their drawbacks. Both require for the researcher to have a sampling frame of the population. In other words, you must have all identifying information of each person in the population you are studying to carry out that form of sampling method. For example, if you wanted to survey all students at your university, that would require having the contact information (i.e., emails) for each student.

In such instances, cluster sampling is often used. To carry out cluster sampling, the researcher would first sample groups or clusters of participants rather than all participants. In other words, consider your home state had a total of 500 K–12 schools and you wanted to survey students to determine whether they were being exposed to illegal substances and if so, at what age. Rather than trying to survey all students among the 500 schools, you would randomly select a chosen number (e.g., 20) and then survey those specific schools. This method of sampling often involves a multistage process whereby you sample large clusters, then sample smaller clusters.

Nonprobability Sampling. However, most researchers in the behavioral sciences do not carry out probability sampling. Rather, researchers often rely on **nonprobability sampling**. With this approach, researchers have no way of knowing whether a particular case "Jane Doe" will be chosen from the sample.

- ***Convenience Sampling*** includes participants which are readily available. For example, as a student, how many times have you been given the opportunity to participate in a study by your professor? When your professor sends out the evaluation online, she/he has no way of knowing who will complete the survey but is relying on a group of participants available to them.
- ***Snowball Sampling*** is the process of identifying someone who meets the criteria for inclusion in a study, and then asking this individual if he or she was able to refer or recommend others that would also meet the inclusion criteria so the researcher can contact them.

There are several other examples of nonprobability sampling procedures available, which include modal instance sampling, quota sampling, and expert sampling. Although these methods of sampling procedures are often used in research studies, it is important to be familiar with sampling procedures as often times, scales should be developed on prior peer-reviewed articles and literature. Additionally, scale questions (items) are generally developed based on the literature relevant to the construct. Furthermore, determining if an adequate sample size of participants included in the development of the test/assessment is crucial to determining if you have the ability to generalize the results to the entire population, called **external validity**. There are several types of internal validation methods which scale developers will often use to validate an instrument (test).

Validity

Validity deals with how well a test measures what it claims to measure rather than measuring something else. A well-designed instrument that has strong validity assists a counseling professional in determining whether the findings are genuine and not the result of something else. The validity of a test is related to two questions, including (1) what does the test measure and (2) how well does the test measure the trait/characteristic?

Face validity is the first type of validity that a counseling professional can use to determine whether an instrument could be beneficial to use in practice. Specifically, face validity refers to whether a measure appears to measure what it's intended to. For example, if a counseling professional was interested in using an instrument that measured drinking/drug behavior, but also measured criminal activity, and potential for psychological diagnoses, the test would likely include questions that are not just related to drinking behavior. There are three additional types of validity by which a counseling professional should also pay attention to when evaluating a test manual of an instrument, including content validity, criterion-related validity (concurrent and predictive), and construct validity.

Content validity refers to the extent to which a test represents all components of a given construct. More specifically, content validity involves "the systematic examination of the test content to determine whether it covers a representative sample of the behavior domain to be measured" (Anastasi & Urbina, 1997, p. 114). The process of scale development usually involves individuals who are content experts in the construct or domain of interest. For example, if a test developer was interested in creating a fifth-grade math test, a panel of fifth-grade math teachers would be appropriate because they are able to determine whether the questions are appropriate for students enrolled at that level. Another example could be applied to the scenario regarding the national certification examination discussed in scenario 1. It is important for experts in drug and alcohol counseling (e.g., researchers, clinicians, and treatment administrators) to be included in the development of test items, because they can create questions that measure the knowledge of future drug and alcohol counseling professionals. Using fifth-grade math teachers to create test questions may not fully grasp the knowledge, skills, and abilities that a future certified alcohol and drug counselor must have in order to be a successful clinician. There are four factors that are considered when evaluating content validity:

1. Does the test measure the content domain of interest?
2. Do the test items constitute a representative sample of the behavior we want to measure?
3. Did the method involve defining the content/behavior domain being measured and determine whether test items adequately sample that domain?
4. Were a panel of experts used in the development of test items?

It is also important to consider the panel of experts and evaluate their professional background. Within the test manual, often times the content experts used in the development of test items will be provided with their professional affiliations. It is essential to determine how many experts were used, while also determining if a variety of professional background were used (e.g., drug/alcohol counseling training educators, researchers in this counseling specialty, clinicians).

Criterion-related validity involves demonstrating how test scores are correlated with a particular aspect of a client's behavior outside of the test. This "outside behavior" of interest correlates with performance on the test, such as the general record examination (GRE) which is often used to determine the predictability of success among the applicant if accepted into a graduate program. There are two types of criterion-related validity, including concurrent validity and predictive validity. Concurrent validity refers to establishing the relationship between test score(s) and some aspect of the client's current behavior (concurrent validity deals with diagnosis). Suppose we compared the scores of the national certification examination for addiction counselors and the grades in the addiction courses within their academic training program. We could determine the degree that scores on the certification examination are related to the performance in the addiction-related courses. If we compared the GRE examination to first semester performance in graduate school, we could establish predictive validity. Predictive validity refers to establishing the relationship between test score(s) and some future performance of the client (predictive validity deals with prognosis). Using that GRE example, some researchers have predicted that the higher a student performs on the GRE, the greater the likelihood that he or she will be successful in graduate school. However, there are other factors that are generally included in graduate school success (e.g., social relationships, financial considerations). Predictive validity is basically does the test predict what it is supposed to predict.

Construct validity refers to the extent that the test measures the theoretical construct that it claims to measure (Drummond & Jones, 2010). This is established by examining the correlation coefficient between scores on the test in question and scores on another test that measures the same construct of interest (convergent validity) or a different construct of interest (discriminant validity). Convergent validity should produce positive correlations between tests measuring the same or similar trait/construct. For example, an eighth-grade spelling test should be correlated with other eighth-grade spelling tests. Discriminant validity should produce correlations reflecting weak relationships or negative relationships between tests measuring different traits/constructs (e.g., an eighth-grade spelling test should not be correlated with an eighth-grade math test). Let's pretend a counseling professional was working with a client who uses drugs to escape discomfort associated with large crowds; we might administer the Liebowitz Social Anxiety Scale (Liebowitz, 1987). Earlier research by Liebowitz suggested there are two levels of social anxiety, including fear of social situations and avoidance of social situations. Now suppose that we developed an instrument that included a section that measured both fear and avoidance (social anxiety). We would expect to find a strong positive correlation between the items related to social anxiety of our scale and the Liebowitz Social Anxiety Scale, assuming we administered both scales to the same group of individuals. This process is called convergent validity.

In addition to establishing convergent validity, test developers may be interested in demonstrating how the construct for which the scale measures is not related to another construct (discriminant validity). Using the social anxiety example, if we provided the same client a confidence of public speaking in a large crowd scale, we would expect there to be a negative relationship between both scales. In theory, it would be difficult for a person who has severe social anxiety to be able to speak in front of large audiences. Although this may not be true in every situation, we would expect a negative relationship (as social anxiety increases, confidence in speaking in front of large crowds decreases).

To establish convergent validity, a scale developer should produce positive correlations between tests measuring the same or similar trait/constructs. For example, if a test developer created an instrument to measure psychiatric symptoms that would related to the diagnosis of Bipolar in the *DSM-5*, if this test along with an already established test were given to the same group of individuals, then there should be positive correlation between the items of the two scales. Likewise, discriminant validity should produce correlations reflecting weak relationships or negative relationships between tests measuring different trait/constructs. Remember, the closer a correlation coefficient is to 1 or negative 1, the stronger the relationship. The closer the correlation coefficient is to zero, the weaker the relationship. For example, there is usually a positive relationship between studying for an examination and the grade on the examination. If the correlation coefficient is closer to 1, that means the relationship is strong. If the correlation coefficient was closer to zero, that means the relationship between study time and grade on the examination is weaker in nature.

A *correlation coefficient* is important to understand moving forward in this chapter. A correlation is the measure between two variables and quantifies the degree of association (covariation) between two variables. A correlation describes in numerical terms the degree or strength of the relationship in addition to the direction (i.e., positive or negative as illustrated in Figure 1). The negative or positive portion of the correlation represents the direction of the relationship, but NOT the strength. As one variable increases, the other variable decreases (e.g., as drinking behavior increases, cognitive functioning decreases). A positive correlation indicates that as one variable increases, the other variable increases as well (e.g., as study time increases, the grade on the examination increases). In terms of the strength of the relationship, the closer the coefficient is to negative 1 or positive 1, the stronger the relationship. There is no difference in a negative 1 or positive 1 when examining the strength of the relationship. The closer the coefficient score is to zero, the weaker the relationship (zero = no correlation).

Correlation Coefficient
Shows Strength & Direction of Correlation

Figure 1.

Reliability

Reliability refers to the extent to which a scale produces consistent results, if the measurements are repeated (Howell, 2009). Another way to think about reliability is whether the instrument consistently measures what it is intended to measure or if you measure the same thing would you get the same score? Consider stepping on a weight scale and you weigh yourself every evening for the past week. You would expect for the scale to be within at least a five-pound range, but what if Monday you weighed 125 pounds and Friday you weighed 180 pounds? Would your scale be reliable? We will be discussing three ways that a test developer may measure reliability, including (1) internal consistency, (2) test–retest reliability, and (3) parallel-forms reliability. Each type of reliability analyses produces a score ranging from 0.00 to 1.00, with higher scores indicating higher accuracy. The observed score produced from each of these types of analyses is composed of a person's true score and error. An instrument is said to be reliable if it accurately reflects the true score and minimizes the error component. The closer the observed score is to the numerical value of 1, it is presumed that the error decreases. Several scholars will argue that there is a relationship between reliability and validity. Specifically, it is important for a valid test to accurately measure what it intends to measure. As can be ascertained from the image below, a test can be reliable but not valid. In the first image of the bull's-eye, one can have high accuracy and precision, but may not hit the target in the location that is desired. Another way to view concept is to consider the scores on the national drug/alcohol certification examination and how the test may be reliable, but it might not measure all of the content areas that it claims to. Specifically, if the examination consists of questions which focus on a clinical diagnosis of schizophrenia rather than substance abuse, then the test does not measure what it is intended to measure. The second bull's-eye demonstrates how a scale can measure a construct of interest, but the results may not be consistent. A test may not be valid or reliable as the construct has not been accurately measured, and the questions may be poorly written, which could increase error associated with the test (decreasing the reliability coefficient). The final bull's-eye represents what the desired instrument should be, in terms of being both reliable and valid.

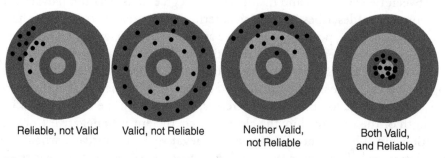

Reliable, not Valid   Valid, not Reliable   Neither Valid, not Reliable   Both Valid, and Reliable

Figure 2.

In addition to evaluating the validity of a test when selecting an instrument to use in practice, additional considerations consist of the following: (a) determine if the test/user manual discusses reliability and (b) examine the reliability score to determine how consistent the test is. There are other types of reliability (e.g., inter-rater/observer reliability) that may be used in other types of research; however, these will not be discussed in this chapter.

Internal consistency is used to assess the consistency of results across items within a test, or how well the items on a test measure the same construct or idea. Test developers will determine the appropriate type of statistical analysis appropriate to measure reliability depending on the level of measurement used and the type of reliability being measured. There are three primary types of statistical procedures that are primarily used by instrument developers to measure internal consistency, including Cronbach's alpha and the split-half procedure (measured by Spearman and Brown formula, and/or Guttmann's formula). It may be difficult for a counseling professional to determine if each of the reliability procedures immediately above was conducted properly, but a counseling professional should still be able to determine if the reliability of the instrument is adequate. The table below is a visual depiction of the internal consistency categories based on the Cronbach alpha score.

Researchers have long argued what score is necessary for an instrument to be reliable instrument. However, the closer the score is to 1, the higher the reliability. A minimum of 0.7 should be the cutoff point in most instances, but a counseling professional should aim at a 0.8 or higher. Remember, the lower the reliability score, the greater the error (or the less likely you are to get the same score if you are administered the test again). Also, if the test manual of an instrument indicates an instrument's reliability was 1.0 (perfect reliability), a counseling professional should become skeptical as there is usually always error associated in statistics and a perfect reliability score is near impossible.

The **split-half** procedure is the process of dividing the test into equivalent halves in order to form two sets of items. The entire test is administered to the group of individuals, and the total score for each set of items is computed. The split-half reliability score is obtained by determining the correlation between the two sets. This is beneficial because the test is only being administered once, thus lessening the potential of time sampling error (as discussed in the test–retest reliability section below). It must be noted that splitting the test into the "first" and "second" half is not advised because of time sampling error (fatigue) and content sampling error (difficulty of items). Therefore, an odd-even split of items is one method to produce scores for each participant (Drummond & Jones, 2010). Longer tests generally produce stronger reliability, but the split-half reliability function reduces the number of items by 50 percent. Therefore, the Spearman-Brown formula for calculating the reliability correlation coefficient is used because it adjusts for the decrease in the number of items (Huck, 2011). Other types of internal consistency analyses include the Kuder–Richardson procedure (commonly used) or kappa (k), which are also used to analyze nominal level data. Weighted

Table 2 Internal Consistency Categories

Cronbach's Alpha	Internal Consistency
$\alpha \geq 0.9$	Excellent
$0.9 > \alpha \geq 0.8$	Good
$0.8 > \alpha \geq 0.7$	Acceptable
$0.7 > \alpha \geq 0.6$	Questionable
$0.6 > \alpha \geq 0.5$	Poor
$0.5 > \alpha$	Unacceptable

Kappa techniques are used to analyze ordinal level data, and intraclass correlation coefficients and internal consistency reliability coefficients are used to analyze interval or ratio level data (Fitzpatrick et al., 2011).

Test–retest reliability is a mechanism where a group of people are administered a test, and then at a later point, readministered the same test. The two test administrations can occur over a short period of time such as a day, or as long as a year or even more. The researcher's primary goal is correlate the two sets of scores to assess for consistency (Drummond & Jones, 2010). The resulting correlation coefficient will examine the two sets of scores with the final score describing the degree of reliability. Moreover, one would expect the score on each test to be similar since the same individuals are being tested. However, some problems may arise from this type of reliability analyses, including (a) differences in performance on the second test may actually change due to the first test [e.g., the test taker learns new information and their responses change]; (b) constructs of interest may change over time independent of the stability of the measure; (c) the interval between the two administrations of the test may be too long and the construct you are attempting to measure may have changed; or (d) the interval may be too short, which causes the reliability to be inflated because of memory. Additionally, the test developer may have difficulty in making sure the testing environment is identical between both samples.

Parallel or alternate forms are used to assess the consistency of results of two tests constructed in the same way from the same content domain (Fitzpatrick et al., 2011). Both tests must have the same rules for administration, the same number of items, items should be in the same format, and the range and level of difficulty should be equal for both tests. Essentially, parallel or alternate forms means that there are two versions of a test where questions for each form measure the construct of interest. For example, certifications examinations (e.g., NCCAP level-2 certification examination) oftentimes have more than one version of the examination with questions from each version being similar to each other (e.g., difficulty of the questions, construct being measured). This is beneficial because if a test taker needs to retake a certification examination, the questions will not be identical to the previous version, thus eliminating some learning of specific answers to test items (learning may have occurred due to additional studying, but not for specific test items). In terms of reliability, an instrument developer would provide each version of the examination to the same sample of people within a short time period. The correlation coefficient is then observed by the test developer to determine how reliable each form is (remember, the closer to 1.00, the more reliable).

Statistical Concepts

Statistics is a branch of mathematics that provides the tools for analyzing numerical data in a method (Howell, 2009). Descriptive statistics are used to organize, summarize, and present data in a systematic fashion (Trochim et al., 2014), while inferential statistics include procedures for reaching tentative conclusions from data using probability theory. Descriptive statistics include frequency distributions, measures of central tendency, and variability. A frequency distribution is to accomplish the task of organizing, summarizing, and describing data (collections of measurements). For example, when evaluating the test manual, the data should be organized and summarized in a manner that the counseling professional can observe the characteristics (e.g., gender, race, age, educational background) of the sample of the population that participated in taking the survey.

The *measures of central tendency* represent an average or typical value of the data (mean, mode, median), and described the central point of the distribution, while variability describes how the scores are scattered around the central point. The mean is the average of the scores of the participants. This is accomplished by adding up all of the numbers (scores), and then dividing by how many numbers there are.

Example: 2, 4, 5, 3, 4, 2, 1, 5, 6, 7, 4, 3
Step 1: Add up the numbers (2+4+5+3+4+2+1+5+6+7+4+ 3) = 46
Step 2: Divide by the count (how many numbers) = 46/12 = 3.83

The mode is the most frequently occurring score. If there is one mode, it is considered unimodal. Whereas, having two modes is bimodal. Having more than two modes is multimodal. Below are two examples as represented in Table 3:

The median is the score that divides the distribution into two parts such that an equal number of scores falls above and below that point (Trochim et al., 2014). The formula to calculate the median is $(N + 1) / 2 = n^{th}$ digit. The first step is to rewrite the number so they are in order from smallest to largest.

Numbers: 10, 11, 5, 14, 22, 32, 15, 17, 13
Rewrite: 5, 10, 11, 13, 14, 15, 17, 22, 32

Note: There are nine numbers in the list, so the middle one will be the $(9 + 1) \div 2 = 10 \div 2 = $ 5th number.

There is statistical software that a test developer will use to calculate these numbers. However, it may be beneficial to counseling professionals to know what these numbers mean. The *measure of variability* represents the dispersion of scores about the average value (Howell, 2009). The goal is to obtain a measure of how spread out the scores are in a distribution. A measure of variability usually accompanies a measure of central tendency as basic descriptive statistics for a set of scores. This allows a scale developer to measure how accurately any individual score represents the entire population. The smaller the variability, the closer the scores are clustered together and will provide a good representation of the entire data set (Drummond & Jones, 2010). The range, interquartile range, and variance and standard deviation is how variability of the data can be measured.

The *range* is the maximum score minus the minimum score and is affected by extreme values. This represents the total distance covered by the distribution. The *interquartile range* is the distance covered by the middle 50% of the distribution (difference between quartile 1 and quartile 3). The figure below represents a normal distribution. The range would represent the highest score on the test minus the lowest score on the test. The normal distribution represents the population, where 68% of the population would be between −1 and 1 standard deviations, 95% of the population would be between −2 and 2 standard deviations, and 99.7% of the population would be between 3 standard deviations. Standard deviations represent the distance from the mean, median, and mode (in a normal distribution). In a normal distribution, most cases cluster in the center of the range and the number of cases decreases as extremes are approached, and the curve is bilaterally symmetrical with a single peak in the center (Howell, 2009).

Most human traits approximate the normal curve (e.g., height, weight, intelligence, academic achievement, aptitudes, and personality). For example, suppose researchers were attempting to establish guidelines to what appropriate weight is based on a person's biological sex, age, and race. These researchers would need to have a representative sample for each of these categories.

Table 3 Measures of Central Tendency

Value	Frequency	Total
13	1, 1, 1, 1	4
14	1, 1	2
16	1	1
18	1	1
21	1	1

Note: One Mode (Unimodal): 13, 13, 13, 13, 14, 14, 16, 18, 21 = <u>**Mode = 13**</u>

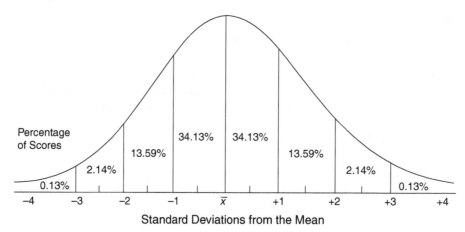

Figure 3.
Adapted from Mark Leary–*Introduction to Behavioral Research Methods, 6th ed*, 2012.

Standard scores allow for comparing an individual's raw score to others who have taken the same test. There are several types of standard scores, including Z-scores, T-scores, Stanines, CEEB scores, Deviation IQs, and percentiles. In norm reference testing, we compare a person to others, as described above and represented in the standard scores mentioned in the prior sentence. A "norm" is the average performance and is established by administering the test to a large representative sample of people for whom the test was designed. After collecting the data, researchers would create a normal distribution (evaluating the measures of central tendency and dispersion) to determine what a normal range is. As displayed in the figure above, 68% would fall between −1 and 1 standard deviations. For test development, establishing a normal distribution is helpful as we can observe whether an individual is considered "normal" on the construct that is being measured. Percentile rankings or scores are another method of evaluating an individual. A percentile rank informs how well an individual has performed compared to other people. For example, a percentile rank score of 99 on the national certification examination would indicate a test taker as scoring higher than 98 percent of the people that have taken the test. Without standardizing the scores of the sample, it would be difficult to make comparisons. A normal distribution, as mentioned above, will result in a sample of test subjects as representative of the population, and with a relatively large sample. Standard scores assist in the interpretation of an individual's test (raw) score, show how an individual's score fits within the total distribution of scores, and create a technique for comparison (Howell, 2009).

Chapter Activity

Identify an assessment that is used in the treatment of people with drug or alcohol challenges (e.g., Global Appraisal of Individual Needs [GAIN], Addiction Severity Index [ASI]). Locate the test manual for the assessment that you have chosen. Using the checklist below, answer the following categories: Basic Information, Background Information, Psychometric Properties of the Test. Determine based on the information provided in the chapter whether this is an instrument that is reliable and valid, and could be used in practice. With a classmate, practice administering your instrument by following the specific instructions in the test manual. After administering the test, answer the questions in the category of Administration of the Test, and Scoring and Interpretation of the Test. Once this is complete, reevaluate all of the completed categories and provide your overall impression of the test you have selected. Although this process may seem time-consuming, it will provide for the appropriate selection of a test to be used within clinical practice.

Checklist

Although a counseling professional may feel overwhelmed when selecting a test to use in clinical practice, the checklist below may be helpful in evaluating each test in the areas covered above.

Basic Information

- Name of test selected
- Author(s) and developer(s) of the test
- How/where can the test be purchased?
- Is computer software available for scoring and interpretation?
- Cost of test and materials
- User qualifications for the test

Background Information on the Test

- Purpose of test
- Nature of the Test Items
- Target population for the test
- Age and reading level requirements of examinees
- Standardization procedures

Psychometric Properties of the Test

- Discuss the norm sample
- Discuss the Reliability of the Test
- Discuss the Validity of the Test

Administration of Test

- Were the instructions easy to follow and easy for the "client" to understand?
- How were questions by the "client" handled?
- Describe the ease and thoroughness of the test manual.
- Describe the testing environment and administration time.

Scoring and Interpretation of Test

- How well does the test manual explain scoring procedures?
- Was the test easy to score and interpret?
- Report the test scores for your client.
- What do the results indicate?
- What are the implications of the results for your client?
- What are the limitations, if any, of the test results?
- What recommendations would you make for the client?

Overall Impression of the Test

- What is your opinion of the psychometric properties of the test?
- How would you rate the quality of the test manual and materials?
- What, if any, difficulties did you encounter administering and/scoring the test?
- Did the results for your "client" surprise you in any way?
- Is this test useful for counseling professionals?
- Describe any ethical concerns you have about this test.
- Discuss any cultural fairness issues.

References

Anastasi, A., & Urbina, S. (1997). *Psychological testing* (7th ed.). Upper Saddle River, NJ: Prentice Hall.

Drummond, R., & Jones, K. (2010). *Assessment procedures for counselors and helping professionals* (7th ed.). Upper Saddle River, NJ: Pearson.

Fitzpatrick, J. L., Sanders, J. R., & Worthen, B. R. (2011). *Program evaluation: Alternative approaches and practical guidelines* (4th ed.). Boston, MA: Pearson Education.

Howell, D. (2009). *Statistical methods for psychology.* New York, NY: Cengage Wadsworth.

Huck, S. W. (2011). *Reading statistics and research* (6th ed.). New York, NY: Pearson.

Liebowitz, M. R. (1987). Social phobia. *Modern Problems of Pharmacopsychiatry, 22,* 141–173.

National Certification Addiction Counselor Levels. (2018). National Certification Commission for Addiction Professionals. Retrieved from https://www.naadac.org/certification

Sommers-Flanagan, J., & Sommers-Flanagan, R. (2017). *Clinical interviewing* (7th ed.). Hoboken, NJ: Wiley & Sons.

Trochim, W. M. K., Donnelly, J. P., & Arora, K. (2014). *The research methods: The essential knowledge base* (3rd ed.). Boston, MA: Cengage Learning.

Chapter 4

Screening for Substance-Related Disorders

Sharon J. Davis

Key Terms: screening, assessment, reliability, validity

Key Objectives: After reading this chapter, students will be able to (a) identify the purpose of a screening instrument and (b) implement a reliable and valid SUD screen.

The first step in client assessment is client screening. According to the Substance Abuse and Mental Health Services Administration (SAMHSA), screening is a method of "quickly assessing the severity of substance use" and identifying the appropriate level of treatment (SAMHSA, n.d). Simply put, the purpose of a screen is to determine if substance use problems actually exist (Capuzzi & Stauffer, 2008). When a person seems to be presenting with symptoms of a substance use disorder (SUD), but there is not enough evidence to order a full assessment, a screening instrument can be a quick and cost-effective way to rule out the need for further assessment. In cases where there are drug or alcohol problems, however, the screening process can help counselors to know when to request a comprehensive assessment or whether to provide brief intervention or make a referral to treatment (Capuzzi & Stauffer, 2008). Keep in mind, screening instruments provide only a minimal amount of information about a client. Counselors must always be careful not to confuse a screening with an assessment. An assessment is a comprehensive process which is done by a trained professional to determine a client's diagnosis and treatment plan needs (SAMHSA, 2017). An assessment may include a screening instrument, but a single screening instrument is never enough to be considered an assessment. Typical assessments will include several sources of information on your client. This may include collateral information from previous treatment providers and referral sources, one or more screening instruments, family and significant others, and the client interview. A diagnosis should be based on several sources of information, never just a single test score. This chapter will focus specifically on screening for SUDs.

A typical screening instrument only takes 5–10 minutes to complete. The screening process is efficient and cost-effective, which makes it ideal in sorting out individuals at actual risk for having a SUD from those who do not need services. It would be unrealistic and incredibly time-consuming for comprehensive SUD assessments to be routinely given to the general public. SAMHSA suggests that people with little or no risky behavior and with low screening scores do not need an actual SUD intervention; however, they may still benefit from more universal prevention programs. Individuals with moderate screening scores will likely benefit from a brief intervention program, and comprehensive assessment and SUD treatment should be reserved for those with high screening scores (SAMHSA, 2013).

As a counselor, it will be your responsibility to choose reliable and valid screening instruments to use on your clients. Screening instruments are always short and limited in the information they give you. The best use of a screening instrument is to identify areas where the client may have needs which should then be given a more thorough assessment. Screening instrument responses can serve as a "red flag" that highlights a possible client issue. It would be unethical to apply a diagnosis to a client based only on a screening result.

Prescreening

Sometimes a counselor or other professional may meet a person they suspect might have a drug or alcohol use problem, but there is very little time for screening. This is when a prescreening might be more convenient. Prescreenings are shortened versions of screenings. They may even consist of only one question. There are few validated prescreening instruments, however, so as a counselor you will want to choose wisely. SAMHSA (2013) suggests the AUDIT-C or the NIAAA prescreening tools. The Alcohol Use Disorders Identification Test-Consumption (AUDIT-C) is a validated prescreen which uses the first three questions of the 10-item AUDIT questionnaire. The AUDIT is discussed later on in this chapter.

The National Institute on Alcohol Abuse and Alcoholism (NIAAA) prescreen consists of only one question which varies based on gender. For males ask, "how many times in the past year have you had 5 drinks or more in a day?" For females ask, "how many times in the past year have you had 4 drinks or more in a day?" Five drinks in a day is considered heavy drinking for males, but for females it only takes four drinks. A similar single question can be used to prescreen for illicit drug use. It is "how many times in the past year have you used an illegal drug or used a prescription medication for nonmedical reasons?" If a person can answer never to any of these questions, a screening is probably not necessary.

When to Use a Screening

As a counselor, you will have to decide between prescreenings, screenings, and assessments. Prescreenings are rarely used, but certainly can save the most amount of time. They also provide the least amount of information, however. When in doubt, choose a screening over a prescreening. There are many situations where it would be prudent to do a screening for SUD rather than a full assessment. Screenings are fast to do, but provide limited information about a client. It may be helpful for a counselor to use a screening to identify a client who might have a SUD, but has not had a full SUD assessment. For example, let's say you are providing mental health counseling to a client and you suspect they may have a drug or alcohol problem. Screenings are also useful during crisis interventions involving clients the counselor is unfamiliar with. For example, imagine you have been called to the local emergency room to assess a person who is suicidal, but you suspect they may also have a co-occurring SUD. Screenings are typically very simple to use and require little training; therefore, oftentimes they are conducted by noncounseling professionals.

SBIRT

Since 2003, an initiative known as SBIRT has received a lot of attention. Screenings can be useful across multiple settings. The Screening, Brief Intervention, and Referral to Treatment (SBIRT) initiative has been popular for a number of years. SBIRT is a public health approach designed to provide universal screening and early intervention and treatment services for those with SUDs, as well as prevention of

SUD in communities. SBIRT trains providers across various disciplines to perform drug and alcohol screenings and to provide brief interventions when needed. Brief interventions are time limited (typically one or two sessions) and focus on increasing client insight and awareness regarding substance use. Brief interventions can also be used to increase client motivation and readiness to change. The brief intervention method can be used by providers who are not counselors. SBIRT programs train these providers in how to do a brief intervention. In the case of more severe client needs, the providers are trained in how to make an appropriate referral to SUD treatment.

Providers implementing a SBIRT program screen all of the individuals they come in contact with, regardless of suspicion of SUD. For example, a physician using SBIRT would give all of their patients a substance use screen even when the patient was not presenting with SUD symptoms. SBIRT is meant to provide *universal screening*. SBIRT screening typically only takes 5–10 minutes and you do not have to be a licensed counselor to use these instruments. This is important since physicians usually do not have time to provide patients with a lengthy screening. Any patient with a positive score on a drug or alcohol screen would then be provided with a brief intervention by the healthcare facility. If a brief intervention alone was not adequate in addressing the patient's substance use, then the physician would make a referral to a SUD treatment provider. SBIRT has been used successfully by hospitals, state cooperatives, and colleges (SAMHSA, 2013).

What to Look for in a Screen

A screening instrument needs to be sensitive, specific, reliable, and valid (Capuzzi & Stauffer, 2008). Sensitivity refers to the ability of a screen to accurately provide the counselor with a true positive result. That is, if a person really has a SUD, will the screen detect it? Specificity refers to the ability of a screen to yield a true negative. For example, if a client does not actually have a SUD the screening result will be negative. A good screen can detect those with an actual SUD and rule out those who do not. Both these concepts are related to a screening instrument's reliability and validity.

Reliability is a screen's consistency in results. If a screen is reliable it will give you the same results time after time. As an example, if your client has an alcohol use disorder, a good screening instrument will yield a positive result each time you administer it. Validity refers to the screen's ability to measure what it is designed to measure. For example, a screen that is supposed to detect possible alcohol use disorder should actually measure a possible alcohol use disorder and not some other disorder. As a counselor, it will be your responsibility to use screening instruments that have all of these qualities. A good screening instrument will have this information in its manual or in published research study results. Also, as a counselor you should be aware of the source of the instrument you have chosen. As a general rule, if you find a "screening instrument" on a social media site it is probably not an acceptable choice. Look for reputable sources when selecting screens. For example, both SAMHSA and the National Institute on Drug Abuse (NIDA) are good sources for screening materials available to counselors. In this chapter, I will introduce you to some screening instruments which have been shown to have high reliability and validity.

Examples of Instruments

The NIDA Drug Use Screening Tool

The NIDA Drug Use Screening Tool is a 1- to 7-item questionnaire adapted by the NIDA. It is based on the World Health Organization's (WHO, 2008) screening instrument known as the ASSIST. This questionnaire is available in electronic format and is appropriate for screening of drug and alcohol use in adults. The screening is available for free at https://www.drugabuse.gov/nmassist/.

The GAIN-SS

A highly respectable agency which develops assessment and screening materials is Chestnut Health Systems. Dr. Michael Dennis and the staff at Chestnut Health Systems have developed a series of instruments known as the Global Appraisal of Individual Needs (GAIN). The first of these instruments was created in 1993. They have full assessment instruments (like the GAIN-I) and screening instruments, like the GAIN-SS (or Short Screener). However, Chestnut Health Systems does require a counselor to go through training and certification to use their instruments.

This screen can be used as part of an SBIRT program or by counselors. Training in using the GAIN-SS takes about 60 minutes and more information on becoming trained can be found online at http://gaincc.org/instruments. The GAIN-SS consists of 23 items and takes about 10 minutes to administer. The 23 items are divided into four sections: Internalizing Disorders, Externalizing Disorders, Crime/violence, and Substance Use Disorders. The GAIN-SS has been shown to have good reliability and validity (Dennis, Chan, & Funk, 2006; Dennis, Feeney, Hanes-Stevens, & Bedoya, 2008). Examples of items from each section in GAIN-SS include:

Internalizing Disorder:

Example: When was the last time you had significant problems with feeling very trapped, lonely, sad, blue, depressed, or hopeless about the future?

Externalizing Disorder:

Example: When was the last time you did the following things two or more times: lied or conned to get things you wanted or to avoid having to do something?

Substance Use Disorder:

When was the last time you spent a lot of time either getting alcohol or other drugs, using alcohol or other drugs, or recovering from the effects of alcohol or other drugs?

Crime/Violence:

When was the last time you had a disagreement in which you pushed, grabbed, or shoved someone?

Each item on the GAIN-SS is answered with responses of never, past month, 2–3 months ago, 4–12 months ago, or 1 year ago. For more information on accessing the GAIN materials, please contact the GAIN Coordinating Center at Chestnut Health Systems (http://gaincc.org/).

The SASSI

The Substance Abuse Subtle Screening Instrument (SASSI) includes both alcohol and drug related questions. It takes 10–15 minutes to complete. This screen consists of two groups of items—subtle items and risk prediction scale items. There are 52 items which are described as "subtle" because they refer to a variety of nondrug and alcohol behaviors related to health, emotional states, social interactions, interests, needs, values, and preferences. The risk prediction scales include 12 alcohol-related items and 14 drug-related items. The risk prediction scale items are also called the "face valid" items because it is obvious that they are measuring drug or alcohol problems.

The SASSI was developed by Glen A. Miller in 1985 and revised in 1999. There is no training required to use it; however, it is a copyrighted instrument which requires a fee for its use. Counselors can find more information about obtaining the SASSI by contacting the SASSI Institute through their website: www .sassi.com. The SASSI has been shown to have good reliability and validity.

CAGE and CAGE-AID

One of the shortest screening tools available is the CAGE. It consists of just four questions. The CAGE was developed by Ewing (1984) and published in the *Journal of the American Medical Association*. This screen is available for counselors to use for free and no training is required. The original CAGE was used to screen for possible alcohol use disorder. For each "yes" response the client gives, one point is given. Any score of 2 or higher indicates problem drinking. Remember, however, a screening instrument cannot be used to yield a diagnosis. The items on the CAGE measure 1) has the client ever felt they need to cut down on their use of alcohol, 2) if they have been annoyed by other people's criticism of their drinking, 3) if they have ever felt guilty because of their use of alcohol, and 4) have they ever drank in the morning to get themselves up and going.

The CAGE-AID was adapted to include drug use. It was developed by Brown and Rounds in 1995. Scoring of the CAGE-AID is the same as for the CAGE, but the questions are slightly different. The CAGE-AID is free for counselors to use and can be found online at https://www.integration.samhsa .gov/clinical-practice/screening-tools#drugs.

AUDIT

Another easy to use screen is the AUDIT. The Alcohol Use Disorders Identification Test (AUDIT), developed in 1982 by the WHO, is a simple way to screen and identify people at risk of alcohol problems. This screen can also be used with no formal training and at no cost. The AUDIT consists of 10 questions and is scored by adding up the corresponding numbers listed by the responses. A score of 8 or more on the AUDIT indicates the client might have an alcohol use disorder. A counselor would want to use any positive AUDIT result to identify clients who need a more thorough assessment.

Alcohol Use Disorders Identification Test (AUDIT)

1. **How often do you have a drink containing alcohol?**
   (0) Never (Skip to Questions 9–10)
   (1) Monthly or less
   (2) 2 to 4 times a month
   (3) 2 to 3 times a week
   (4) 4 or more times a week

2. **How many drinks containing alcohol do you have on a typical day when you are drinking?**
   (0) 1 or 2
   (1) 3 or 4
   (2) 5 or 6
   (3) 7, 8, or 9
   (4) 10 or more

3. **How often do you have six or more drinks on one occasion?**
   (0) Never
   (1) Less than monthly
   (2) Monthly
   (3) Weekly
   (4) Daily or almost daily

4. **How often during the last year have you found that you were not able to stop drinking once you had started?**
   (0) Never
   (1) Less than monthly
   (2) Monthly
   (3) Weekly
   (4) Daily or almost daily

5. **How often during the last year have you failed to do what was normally expected from you because of drinking?**
   (0) Never
   (1) Less than monthly
   (2) Monthly
   (3) Weekly
   (4) Daily or almost daily

6. **How often during the last year have you been unable to remember what happened the night before because you had been drinking?**
   (0) Never
   (1) Less than monthly
   (2) Monthly
   (3) Weekly
   (4) Daily or almost daily

7. **How often during the last year have you needed an alcoholic drink first thing in the morning to get yourself going after a night of heavy drinking?**
   (0) Never
   (1) Less than monthly
   (2) Monthly
   (3) Weekly
   (4) Daily or almost daily

8. **How often during the last year have you had a feeling of guilt or remorse after drinking?**
   (0) Never
   (1) Less than monthly
   (2) Monthly
   (3) Weekly
   (4) Daily or almost daily

9. **Have you or someone else been injured as a result of your drinking?**
   (0) No
   (2) Yes, but not in the last year
   (4) Yes, during the last year
10. **Has a relative, friend, doctor, or another health professional expressed concern about your drinking or suggested you cut down?**
    (0) No
    (2) Yes, but not in the last year
    (4) Yes, during the last year

Add up the points associated with answers. A total score of 8 or more indicates harmful drinking behavior.

DAST

The Drug Abuse Screening Test (DAST) was developed by Harvey Skinner in 1982. The DAST consists of 20 questions and is designed to measure possible drug use disorders. It is available in both adult and adolescent versions. The DAST is easy to use and to score. There is also a convenient 10-item version of the DAST. It is recommended by SAMHSA and can be found at https://www.integration.samhsa.gov/clinical-practice/screening-tools#drugs.

ASSIST

The Alcohol, Smoking, and Substance Involvement Screening Test (ASSIST) is an 8-item screening instrument developed by the WHO. It was designed to screen for substance use in primary care and medical settings. It is available in several languages and is easy to administer and score. Patients use response cards to answer each question. This makes it especially easy to give. And each patient is given a report card after scoring, so they can understand their results. There is no fee or training required to use this screening; however, it does include a manual for use in primary care which should be followed. The questionnaire instructions, items, response card, and report card examples are as follows.

Alcohol, Smoking, and Substance Involvement Screening Test

INTRODUCTION: I am going to ask you some questions about your experience with alcohol, tobacco products, and other drugs across your lifetime and in the past 3 months. These substances can be smoked, swallowed, snorted, inhaled, injected, or taken in pill form (*Show Drug & Response Card*).

Some of the substances listed may be prescribed by a doctor (like sedatives, pain medications, amphetamines, etc.). For this interview, I will not record medications that are used as prescribed by your doctor. However, if you have taken such drugs for reasons other than prescription, or taken them more frequently or at higher doses than prescribed, please let me know. While I am interested in knowing about your use of various illicit drugs, please be assured that the information on such use will be treated as strictly confidential.

In your life, which of the following substances have you ever used? (*non-medical use only*)	No	Yes	In the past three months, how often have you used the substances mentioned (*first drug, second drug, etc.*)?	Never	Once or Twice	Monthly	Weekly	Daily or Almost Daily
a. Tobacco products	0	3	a. Tobacco products	0	2	3	4	6
b. Alcoholic beverages	0	3	b. Alcoholic beverages	0	2	3	4	6
c. Marijuana	0	3	c. Marijuana	0	2	3	4	6
d. Cocaine or Crack	0	3	d. Cocaine or Crack	0	2	3	4	6
e. Amphetamines or Stimulants	0	3	e. Amphetamines or Stimulants	0	2	3	4	6
f. Inhalants	0	3	f. Inhalants	0	2	3	4	6
g. Sedatives or Sleeping Pills	0	3	g. Sedatives or Sleeping Pills	0	2	3	4	6
h. Hallucinogens	0	3	h. Hallucinogens	0	2	3	4	6
i. Heroin, Morphine, Pain Medication	0	3	i. Heroin, Morphine, Pain Medication	0	2	3	4	6
j. Other, specify:	0	3	j. Other, specify:	0	2	3	4	6

Probe if all answers are negative: "Not even when you were in school?" If "No" to all items, stop the interview.

If "Yes" to any of these items, ask Question 2 for each substance ever used.

If Never to all items in Question 2, skip to Question 6. If any substance in Question 2 was used in the previous 3 months continue with Questions 3, 4, and 5 for each substance used.

During the past three months, how often have you had a strong desire or urge to use (*first drug, second drug, etc.*)?	Never	Once or Twice	Monthly	Weekly	Daily or Almost Daily
a. Tobacco products	0	3	4	5	6
b. Alcoholic beverages	0	3	4	5	6
c. Marijuana	0	3	4	5	6
d. Cocaine or Crack	0	3	4	5	6
e. Amphetamines or Stimulants	0	3	4	5	6
f. Inhalants	0	3	4	5	6
g. Sedatives or Sleeping Pills	0	3	4	5	6
h. Hallucinogens	0	3	4	5	6
i. Heroin, Morphine, Pain Medication	0	3	4	5	6
j. Other, specify:	0	3	4	5	6

During the past three months, how often has your use of (*first drug, second drug, etc.*) led to health, social, legal, or financial problems?	Never	Once or Twice	Monthly	Weekly	Daily or Almost Daily
a. Tobacco products	0	4	5	6	7
b. Alcoholic beverages	0	4	5	6	7
c. Marijuana	0	4	5	6	7
d. Cocaine or Crack	0	4	5	6	7
e. Amphetamines or Stimulants	0	4	5	6	7
f. Inhalants	0	4	5	6	7
g. Sedatives or Sleeping Pills	0	4	5	6	7
h. Hallucinogens	0	4	5	6	7
i. Heroin, Morphine, Pain Medication	0	4	5	6	7
j. Other, specify:	0	4	5	6	7

During the past three months, how often have you failed to do what was normally expected of you because of your use of (*first drug, second drug, etc.*)?	Never	Once or Twice	Monthly	Weekly	Daily or Almost Daily
a. Tobacco Products					
b. Alcoholic beverages	0	5	6	7	8
c. Marijuana	0	5	6	7	8
d. Cocaine or Crack	0	5	6	7	8
e. Amphetamines or Stimulants	0	5	6	7	8
f. Inhalants	0	5	6	7	8
g. Sedatives or Sleeping Pills	0	5	6	7	8
h. Hallucinogens	0	5	6	7	8
i. Heroin, Morphine, Pain Medication	0	5	6	7	8
j. Other, specify:	0	5	6	7	8

Ask Questions 6 and 7 for all substances ever used (i.e., those endorsed in Question 1).

Has a friend or relative or anyone else ever expressed concern about your use of (*first drug, second drug, etc.*)?	No, Never	Yes, in the past three months	Yes, but not in the past three months	Have you ever tried and failed to control, cut down or stop using (*first drug, second drug, etc.*)?	No, Never	Yes, in the past three months	Yes, but not in the past three months
a. Tobacco products	0	6	3	a. Tobacco products	0	6	3
b. Alcoholic beverages	0	6	3	b. Alcoholic beverages	0	6	3
c. Marijuana	0	6	3	c. Marijuana	0	6	3
d. Cocaine or Crack	0	6	3	d. Cocaine or Crack	0	6	3
e. Amphetamines or Stimulants	0	6	3	e. Amphetamines or Stimulants	0	6	3
f. Inhalants	0	6	3	f. Inhalants	0	6	3
g. Sedatives or Sleeping Pills	0	6	3	g. Sedatives or Sleeping Pills	0	6	3
h. Hallucinogens	0	6	3	h. Hallucinogens	0	6	3
i. Heroin, Morphine, Pain Medication	0	6	3	i. Heroin, Morphine, Pain Medication	0	6	3
j. Other, specify:	0	6	3	j. Other, specify:	0	6	3

ASSIST

Response Card

a. **Tobacco products** such as cigarettes, chewing tobacco, cigars, etc.
b. **Alcoholic beverages** such as beer, wine, hard liquor, etc.
c. **Marijuana,** pot, grass, reefer, weed, ganja, hash, chronic, gangster, etc.
d. **Cocaine,** coke, blow, snow, flake, toot, crack, rock, etc.
e. **Amphetamines,** speed, Ritalin, ecstasy, X, diet pills, crystal meth, ice, crank, Dexedrine, etc.
f. **Inhalants,** glue, correction fluid, gasoline, butane, paint thinner, lighter fluid, spray paint, poppers, snappers, Rush, Locker Room, Nitrous Oxide, laughing gas, whippets, etc.
g. **Sedatives or sleeping pills,** Valium, Xanax, Librium, Dalmane, Ativan, Halcion, Miltown, Thorazine, Mellaril, Restoril, Rohypnol, roofies, GHB, Liquid X, Liquid E, Mebaral, Nembutal, Seconal, Fiorinal, Amytal, Phenobarbital, Placidyl, Doriden, downers, etc.
h. **Hallucinogens,** LSD, blotter, acid, mushrooms, PCP, angel dust, THC, wet, illy, ketamine, Special K, vitamin K, 2C-B, etc.
i. **Pain medication, Opioids,** codeine, OxyContin, Darvon, Vicodin, Dilaudid, Demerol, Lomotil, Percodan, Talwin-Nx, heroin, morphine, methadone, etc.
j. **Other drug**: Something not listed here? Please specify: _____

Responses for Questions 2–5

Never: not used in the last 3 months

Once or twice: 1 or 2 times in the last 3 months
Monthly: 1 to 3 times in one month
Weekly: 1 to 4 times per week
Daily or almost daily: 5 to 7 days per week

Responses for Questions 6–8

No, Never

Yes, but not in the past 3 months
Yes, in the past 3 months
ASSIST Patient Feedback Report

Substance	Risk Level			Your Score
	Low	Moderate	High	
Tobacco products such as cigarettes, chewing tobacco, cigars, etc.	0–3	4–26	27+	
Alcoholic beverages such as beer, wine, hard liquor, etc.	0–10	11–26	27+	
Marijuana, pot, grass, reefer, weed, ganja, hash, chronic, etc.	0–3	4–26	27+	
Cocaine, coke, blow, snow, flake, toot, crack, rock, etc.	0–3	4–26	27+	
Amphetamines, speed, Ritalin, ecstasy, X, diet pills, crystal meth, ice, crank, Dexedrine, etc.	0–3	4–26	27+	
Inhalants, glue, correction fluid, gasoline, butane, paint thinner, lighter fluid, spray paint, poppers, snappers, Rush, Locker Room, Nitrous Oxide, laughing gas, whippets, etc.	0–3	4–26	27+	
Sedatives or sleeping pills, Valium, Xanax, Librium, Dalmane, Ativan, Halcion, Miltown, Thorazine, Mellaril, Restoril, Rohypnol, roofies, GHB, Liquid X, Liquid E, Mebaral, Nembutal, Seconal, Fiorinal, Amytal, Phenobarbital, Placidyl, Doriden, downers, etc.	0–3	4–26	27+	
Hallucinogens, LSD, blotter, acid, mushrooms, PCP, angel dust, THC, wet, illy, ketamine, Special K, vitamin K, 2C-B, etc.	0–3	4–26	27+	
Pain medication, Opioids, codeine, OxyContin, Darvon, Vicodin, Dilaudid, Demerol, Lomotil, Percodan, Talwin-Nx, heroin, morphine, methadone, etc.	0–3	4–26	27+	
Other Drugs	0–3	4–26	27+	

What do your scores mean?

Low: You are at low risk of health and other problems from your current pattern of use.

Moderate: You are at risk of health and other problems from your current pattern of substance use.

High: You are at high risk of experiencing severe problems (health, social, financial, legal relationship) as a result of your current pattern of use and are likely to be dependent.

SCORING THE ASSIST

Substance Specific Score.

Sum across questions 2–7 for each drug category separately.

For example, the cannabis use score would be: 2c+3c+4c+5c+6c+7c

Maximum score for tobacco = 31

Maximum score for each of the other drug categories = 39

Substance	Assist Score	Risk Level		
		Low	Moderate	High
a. Tobacco products		0–3	4–26	27+
b. Alcoholic Beverages		0–10	11–26	27+
c. Cannabis		0–3	4–26	27+
d. Cocaine		0–3	4–26	27+
e. Amphetamine type stimulants		0–3	4–26	27+
f. Inhalants		0–3	4–26	27+
g. Sedatives or Sleeping Pills		0–3	4–26	27+
h. Hallucinogens		0–3	4–26	27+
i. Opioids		0–3	4–26	27+
j. Other-specify		0–3	4–26	27+

Low Risk—You are at low risk of health and other problems from your current pattern of use.

Moderate Risk—You are at risk of health and other problems from your current pattern of use.

High Risk—You are at high risk of experiencing severe problems (health, social, financial, legal relationship) as a result of your current pattern of use and are likely to be dependent

Global Continuum of Risk Score.

Sum items (questions 1 – 7) + question 8 for all drug classes together. For example,

(Q1a-Q1j) + (Q2a-Q2j) + (Q3a-Q3j) + (Q4a-Q4j) + (Q5b-Q5j) + (Q6a-Q6j) + (Q7a-Q7j) + Q8.

Maximum score = 414

Most ASSIST-related documents, manuals and supporting materials can be found on the WHO, ASSIST Web Site. (http://www.who.int/substance_abuse/activities/assist/en/).

MAST

The Michigan Alcohol Screening Test (MAST) is a 25-item screening tool for detecting consequences associated with alcohol use. This is the instrument from which the previously discussed DAST was adapted. The MAST was first developed in 1971 by Selzer. Other versions of the MAST have also been developed—the 13-item Short MAST and the MAST-G for geriatric populations. The MAST is a simple, self-scoring test that uses simple "yes" "no" items. You can access the MAST for free at https://www.integration.samhsa.gov/clinical-practice/screening-tools#drugs. Items in the MAST measure a variety of alcohol-related problems, including social, legal, emotional, psychological, and behavioral.

Summary/Conclusion

A good screening instrument can provide a starting place for identifying possible client drug or alcohol problems. Screening requires little training and can be done in a variety of settings, including treatment agencies, schools, healthcare clinics, hospitals, and other community agencies. Paraprofessionals and treatment professionals alike can use screenings to help identify persons who may benefit from brief interventions or referrals for assessment and treatment. A screening instrument is not meant to be a diagnostic tool. Only a trained professional using a comprehensive assessment can ethically diagnose a SUD.

Resources

1. For information on SAMHSA approved screening instruments visit: https://www.integration .samhsa.gov/clinical-practice/screening-tools#drugs
2. For information on the latest statistics and research related to drugs and alcohol, including national trends visit: http://www.drugabuse.gov
3. For information on how to obtain GAIN instruments for screening and assessment visit the Global Appraisal of Individual Needs (GAIN) Coordinating Center at: http://gaincc.org/
4. For information on the SBIRT initiative visit: https://www.samhsa.gov/sbirt

Suggested Activity

Have the class break into pairs. Each pair of students should practice using either the DAST, CAGE-AID, or AUDIT on each other. This can be done "role-play" style where the student acting in the role of the client assumes a fictional identity.

References

Brown, R. L., & Rounds, L. A. (1995). Conjoint screening questionnaires for alcohol and drug abuse. *Wisconsin Medical Journal, 94*, 135–140.

Capuzzi,, D, & Stauffer, M. D. (2008). Foundations of Addiction Counseling. Boston, MA: Pearson Education, Inc.

Dennis, M. L., Chan, Y.-F., & Funk, R. (2006). Development and validation of the GAIN Short Screener (GSS) for internalizing, externalizing, and substance use disorders and crime/violence problems among adolescents and adults. *American Journal on Addictions, 15*(Suppl. 1), s80–s91. doi: 10.1080/10550490601006055

Dennis, M. L., Feeney, T., Hanes-Stevens, L., & Bedoya, L. (2008). *GAIN-SS: Global Appraisal of Individual Needs-Short Screener (GAIN-SS) administration and scoring manual version 2.0.3.* Bloomington, IL: Chestnut Health Systems.

Ewing, J. A. (1984). Detecting alcoholism: The CAGE questionnaire. *JAMA: Journal of the American Medical Association, 252*, 1905–1907.

Miller, G. A. (1985, 1999). *The substance abuse subtle screening inventory (SASSI) Manual* (2nd ed.). Springville, IN: The SASSI Institute.

Selzer, M. L. (1971). The Michigan Alcoholism Screening Test (MAST): The quest for a new diagnostic instrument. *American Journal of Psychiatry, 3*, 176–181.

Skinner, H. A. (1982). The Drug Abuse Screening Test. *Addictive Behaviors, 7*(4), 363–371.

Substance Abuse and Mental Health Services Administration. (2013). *Systems-level implementation of screening, brief intervention, and referral to treatment.* Technical Assistance Publication (TAP) Series 33. HHS Publication No. (SMA) 13-4741. Rockville, MD: Author.

Substance Abuse and Mental Health Services Administration. (n.d.). SAMHSA-HRSA Center for Integrated Health Solutions. Retrieved from https://www.integration.samhsa.gov/ clinical-practice/ screening-tools#drugs

Yudko, E., Lozhkina, O., & Fouts, A. (2007). A comprehensive review of the psychometric properties of the Drug Abuse Screening Test. *Journal of Substance Abuse Treatment, 32,* 189–198.

World Health Organization. (2008). The ASSIST Project: Alcohol, smoking, and substance involvement screening test. Retrieved from http://www.who.int/substance_abuse/activities/assist/en/

Chapter 5

Comprehensive Assessment
Sharon J. Davis

Key Terms: norm group, comprehensive, intake, biopsychosocial, co-occurring disorders, mental status exam

Key Objectives: After reading this chapter, students will be able to choose and implement an appropriate assessment instrument.

Assessment begins the moment you meet your client. It is an ongoing process, consisting of multiple pieces of information. An assessment may include screening results, information from referral sources, family input, previous treatment records, and the client interview. During the client interview, counselors will typically use a comprehensive assessment instrument. These are considerably longer and more global than what you would use during a screening. However, just like when choosing a screening instrument, it will be up to you, the counselor, to choose reliable and valid assessment tools.

Important Features of an Assessment Instrument

In Chapter 3, you read about how to identify an assessment that is reliable and valid. These are fundamentally important aspects of a good instrument. Without validity, a counselor cannot know that they are actually assessing what they are intending to assess and without reliability, assessment results cannot be trusted to be consistent across time. When choosing an instrument, look for research results demonstrating that an instrument is both valid and reliable. The results of your assessment serve as the foundation on which the treatment plan is built. Good treatment begins with an accurate assessment.

In addition to validity and reliability, you will also want to choose an assessment with available normative data for representative groups defined by age, race, gender, and type of setting. Normative data will let you know if the assessment instrument is appropriate for the population you serve. For example, if you work with adolescent clients, you will want to use assessment instruments which have been shown to be reliable and valid in assessing adolescents. Without these type of data, you may be using an instrument which is actually only appropriate for adults. Normative data are established when researchers and test developers give an instrument to a sample of people. This sample is known as the "norm group." You will want to ensure that the norm group is representative of the persons you are assessing.

In addition, norm group results help give meaning to test results by providing comparison scores. Let's say you are assessing an individual for treatment, and you give them a test to determine the severity of their alcohol use disorder. Your client's score may have very little meaning if there is no norm group score with which to compare it. For example, your client, Sam, scores a 50 on an alcohol severity test. How do you interpret his score? Is a 50 high, low, or average? Without a norm group, it is impossible to answer this question. However, if you know that the average person with severe alcohol use disorder scores a 50 on the same test you administered to Sam, you will know that Sam likely has a severe alcohol use disorder. Most assessments will include a manual with reliability and validity results, as well as normative data.

It is important for you to familiarize yourself with the assessment manual. Look for instruments with a detailed manual that describes administration and scoring protocols. In addition, be aware that many instrument materials entail a purchasing fee, and some require costly training and licensure.

Last, you will want to choose an assessment that is *comprehensive*. In other words, it needs to measure substance-related disorders plus home life, medical status, mental health, environmental risks and assets, family and peer dynamics, vocational and employment issues, risk behaviors, leisure and recreation, and criminal justice or legal involvement.

The Intake Interview

Client assessment typically takes place during an intake interview. This is usually the client's first session, and therefore it is not only the counselor's first impression of the client, but also the client's first impression of the counseling agency. It is important that clients are treated with respect, dignity, and unconditional positive regard from the moment they walk through the door. The counselor completing the intake interview needs to establish rapport during that first session. A positive intake experience can foster client engagement in the treatment process. The intake interview sets the tone for treatment.

Careful planning and information gathering prior to the client interview is essential to any good assessment. You will want to gather relevant reports from the client's referral source and other treatment providers before meeting the client. Oftentimes, this will not be the first time your client has been seen at your agency. Be sure to look for previous records. After you have read all the collateral information you were able to gather, you will begin to form an initial impression of your client's history. Here is where I would like to caution you to not let yourself become pessimistic about your client before you even meet them. Let's say you discover that your client has been in and out of treatment multiple times and has relapsed over and over again. It may be tempting to be discouraged and think your client will not be successful this time. The information you gather from previous records is useful, but do not let it taint the present experience. Every client should be viewed with fresh optimism with each new treatment admission.

Capuzzi and Stauffer (2008, p. 86) suggest counselors follow 10 steps in their clinical interview. These are:

1. Review referral information
2. Obtain and review previous evaluations
3. Interview the client
4. Gather corroborating material (e.g., family interview)
5. Formulate a hypothesis
6. Make recommendations
7. Create a report and other significant documents
8. Meet with the client about the results
9. Meet with the support system of the client
10. Follow up with recommendations and referrals

How to Assess

There are different styles of assessments, including low-structured, medium-structured, and high-structured. The low-structured assessment is the most casual. It is also referred to as the clinical interview. Oftentimes, a low-structured assessment will consist of an informal information-gathering session. The counselor will know what information they want to gather, but they may not necessarily follow a written script or set of questions. This type of assessment may provide an opportunity for the client to "tell their story" and for the counselor and client to establish some basic rapport; however, it may lack reliability and validity. There is also the chance of skipped information and loss of focus during this type of assessment.

A more structured approach to assessment is recommended to achieve reliable (consistent) and valid (truthful) responses from clients. To explain the difference between medium- and high-structured assessments, let me start with a description of high structured. Assessments which are high structured consist of a set of questions to ask the client and strict rules on how to ask the questions. High-structured assessments do not allow for any deviation from the "script." Even when a client has a question about what an item means, the counselor is not allowed to offer an explanation or clarification. This method has been used often in the area of intelligence testing. A high-structured assessment certainly has its place, but the rigidity of administration may not always lead to the most valid client responses. For example, if a client does not understand a question, they may not give an accurate answer. It is sometimes necessary for the counselor to help clarify what is being asked. This is when a medium-structured assessment makes the most sense. A medium-structured assessment will consist of a set of questions for the counselor to follow, but lacks the rigid rules of a highly structured assessment. A medium structure can yield reliable and valid responses, but also gives room for the counselor to use common sense. The following guidelines for how to administer a medium-structured assessment are adapted from Dennis, White, Titus, and Unsicker (2007).

1. Do not rephrase any items; rather ask them exactly as printed.
2. Ask all items in the same order as they are printed.
3. Do not skip any items.
4. If your client does not understand an item, it is okay to repeat it.
5. Make sure not to suggest answers to the client.
6. You may use introductory or transitional statements to help your client understand the items. For example, "the next set of items refers to the last 30 days."
7. If you need clarification from the client it is okay to use neutral probes such as "can you tell me more about that?"
8. Listen to your client's responses.
9. Lastly, use common sense.

A medium-structured assessment does not allow for paraphrasing or changing the wording of any items. This helps ensure that every client is asked the exact same set of questions. Deviations in wording of items can change the meaning of what is being asked and this could lower the assessment's validity. During a medium-structured assessment, the counselor is allowed to repeat questions or offer definitions and examples to help the client understand what is being asked. The counselor may also ask the client for clarification if they are not sure what the client was trying to say. This can be done directly like "could you repeat that?" or indirectly as in "can you tell me more about that?" or "can you give me an example?"

What to Assess

As humans, our lives are complex and multifaceted. We are physical beings who live in a social world. We go to work, take care of families, take care of ourselves, and often face personal struggles along with everything else. I like to use the analogy of a pie to illustrate how each person's life is made of equally important subparts. The subparts are pieces of our lives; each piece works with the others to make us whole. Every skilled counselor should take a holistic (or comprehensive) approach in treating their clients. Narrowly focusing on just substance use in treatment does not provide adequate assistance to your client. Your client is more than just his or her substance use. He or she may also have psychological, family, vocational, medical, housing, criminal justice, peer concerns, and co-occurring/co-existing disabilities. Each area of your client must be assessed and included in treatment planning to provide holistic care. The biopsychosocial model of substance use disorders (SUDs) matches nicely with a holistic approach to counseling. According to this approach, SUDs are the result of psychological, biological, and social factors, and each of these factors also influences the other.

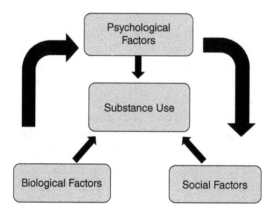

Biological Factors

This is an exciting time to be a substance use counselor. Technological advances in medicine have increased our knowledge of the biological factors associated with the etiology of SUD like never before. In Chapter 1 you learned about many brain factors which are involved in the etiology of SUD. For decades, addiction has been referred to as a "brain disease," but only recently have we been able to use medical technology to prove it.

The reality is that while we have medical devices, like functional magnetic resonance imaging, which allow us to peer into the brains of our clients and "see" their SUD, your typical client will never undergo these types of tests. It would be impractical and expensive to include medical testing as routine parts of a SUD assessment. However, as part of a comprehensive assessment, you will not want to overlook more easily accessible biological or medical information which you can gather directly by asking the client.

Your client may have medical or biological factors affecting his or her life which you need to include in your assessment. For example, what is your client's overall physical health? Does he or she have a co-existing disability? Does he or she have a chronic illness which causes pain and suffering on a daily basis? These types of concerns are important and relevant pieces of your client's life. Imagine a client with chronic back pain. The client's back pain may impact his or her ability to work, exercise, socialize, and even sleep. A client with chronic pain who also has a SUD may struggle with the addictive effects of opioid pain medication while trying to find ways to cope with his or her daily pain management. Or how about a client who cannot work due to a disability? Bill collectors are rarely sympathetic when a person cannot pay bills because of a lack of gainful employment, so an out-of-work client likely has financial problems and resulting stress. Your client's physical health may even contribute to their substance use. He or she may turn to substances to cope with physical problem. Likewise, a client's substance use may exacerbate or cause physical impairments.

Look for assessment instruments that ask questions about your client's health, medical history, current physical problems, and overall health and wellness.

Risk Behaviors

Oftentimes, people with SUD have engaged in other behaviors which may put them at risk for health-related problems and diseases. For example, a client who has been injecting drugs may have used dirty needles and therefore has placed himself or herself at risk for contracting HIV or hepatitis C. Clients may also have engaged in unsafe sexual practices and may have contracted a sexually transmitted disease. These are important factors to ask about during an assessment and to include as part of treatment planning. Many comprehensive assessments will include items which ask about such risky behaviors. And, while it may be uncomfortable to ask a client about his or her sexual behaviors, it is an important part of a comprehensive and holistic assessment.

Psychological Factors and Mental Health

Psychological factors refer to thoughts, feelings, and other cognitive characteristics that affect a person's attitude and behaviors. Researchers have identified many psychological factors related to substance use and recovery. These include personality traits, like thrill seeking, impulsiveness, nonconformity, and aggression (Doweiko, 2012). Also significant are an individual's coping skills, stress, loneliness, self-esteem, boredom, motivation, and readiness to change. For adolescents, attachment to parents, sense of belonging, and adaptability to change are important.

The term "co-occurring disorders" typically refers to a mental health disorder that occurs along with a SUD. According to the Substance Abuse and Mental Health Services Administration (SAMHSA), substance use is the most common co-occurring disorder in people with mental health disorders (SAMHSA, 2009). Depressive disorders, anxiety, schizophrenia, bipolar, and personality disorders are common in people with SUD. In the past, it was the custom for SUD treatment agencies and mental health agencies to treat co-occurring disorders completely separately. In fact, many mental health agencies would refuse to treat a person with a SUD until they got clean and sober and likewise, SUD agencies would turn away clients with untreated mental health issues. Today's evidence-based programs understand that for clients with co-occurring disorders, both issues must be treated simultaneously. Using substances exacerbates or even causes mental health problems, and clients often turn to substance use in order to self-medicate the pain caused by mental health disorders. The two are so intertwined that it seems absurd to treat one before the other. A holistic assessment will include a thorough set of items related to mental health, and, as a counselor, you will want to include mental health in all treatment planning.

Questions to Ask

A thorough assessment of mental and emotional health will include a complete set of questions designed to measure not only the presence of a mental health disorder in those with a co-occurring disorder, but also the emotional needs of all your clients. You will want to ask about any current or past treatment for mental health, along with a series of specific disorder-related questions.

In order to validly measure a mental health disorder in persons with substance use, it is important to rule out symptoms which only occur as a direct result of drug or alcohol use. In other words, if a person experiences psychiatric symptoms only when they are high and the symptoms disappear when they are not high, you can rule out an actual mental health diagnosis. For example, if your client has hallucinations only when on a methamphetamine binge, he or she would not meet criteria for a psychotic disorder. The DSM-5 always requires you rule out mental health diagnoses when the symptoms occur only when substance induced.

Some specific questions include:

1. Have you experienced any significant problems (not related to being high or intoxicated) with the following?
   a. Feeling depressed, down, sad, or blue
   b. Feeling anxious, stressed, or tense
   c. Having trouble understanding, remembering, or concentrating
   d. Hearing voices or seeing things that were not really there
   e. Had trouble controlling violent behavior
   f. Thought about killing yourself or wishing you would die
   g. Attempted suicide

Mental Status Exam

In addition to *questions* to ask your client, you will also make *observations* of your client's current emotional and mental state—this is called a mental status exam. There are a lot of instruments available to measure mental status. Many of these are available free online, but make sure you look for one that is reputable and addresses the following areas:

1. Client Appearance
   How does the client look and behave? For example, are they clean and well-groomed? Is there anything strange or bizarre about their appearance/dress? Do they have any remarkable features, like scars, tattoos, or piercings? Are their movements hyperactive or sluggish?
2. Speech
   How does the client speak? Too fast? Too slow? Too quiet or loud? Is their speech intelligible?
3. Emotions
   What is the client's mood/affect? How does the client appear to be feeling during the interview with you? Are they emotional (crying, angry, fearful, etc.)? Is their affect normal (euthymic), restricted, or flat?
4. Thought process and content
   How does the client think? Does it take them a while to get to the point (circumstantiality)? Do they repeat phrases or return to the same subject (perseveration)? How do they get from one idea to the next (association)?
   What does the client think about? Do they have delusions or compulsive thoughts?
5. Sensory perceptions
   Any hallucinations (auditory, visual, tactile, or olfactory)?
6. Mental capacities
   Are they oriented in time, place, and person? In other words, do they know what day it is, where they are, and who they are?
   What is your estimate of the client's intelligence?
   Can the client remember and concentrate?
   How is the client's judgment and insight?
7. Attitude toward the counselor
   Are they cooperative? Hostile? Defensive? Seductive? Friendly?, etc.

Social

The final piece of the biopsychosocial approach is social. This includes both the social and environmental aspects of your client's life. For example, who are the people in your client's social circle? These include a client's family, friends, peers, co-workers, clergy, and neighbors. On whom does your client rely for social support? Oftentimes, the people in your client's life may provide social support, but is it *sober* social support? As a counselor, you will want to find out what people will be supportive of your client in recovery. These are the individuals who will make up the client's support network.

Family and Peer Support

SUDs impact not only the client, but also the family. According to Family Systems Theory, developed by Murray Bowen, addiction is a family disease. The family unit is like a machine where each part has its role in proper function of the whole. When one part of the machine is broken, the whole system is out of balance. Family members of a person with a SUD have likely experienced pain, suffering, shame, guilt, frustration, and even financial consequences because of their loved one's use. Likewise, a family history of substance use, family dysfunction, and abuse may have played a part in your client's SUD. A supportive family, however, can have an important role in your client's recovery. You will want to ask your client about their family history and interview family members to find out more information about your client. Moreover, including family in treatment can help heal the family system and provide support for your client's recovery.

Peers, co-workers, and other people in your client's social circle have likely been part of their drug use. Your client may associate with people who supply them with substances and who engage in substance use with them. In treatment, clients are often faced with having to avoid the people in their lives who could trigger a relapse. Be sure to ask your client about people they know who are supportive of recovery and any self-help groups (like AA or NA) they may have attended.

Vocational

All too often, substance abuse counselors ignore the importance of employment in a client's life. However, gainful employment is a predictor of treatment success. Your client needs a source of legal income and a sense of purpose. A job can provide both. As a counselor, you should assess vocational and educational history and include career development in your client's treatment. This is a vital piece of "the pie." Your client may need assistance with finding vocational rehabilitation counseling, career counseling, job training, or adult education programs.

Criminal Justice

In substance abuse counseling, many clients are mandated or coerced into treatment. This means your client will likely have some involvement in the criminal justice system. They may have pending charges, probation, or parole requirements. According to research, all levels of treatment (including inpatient, intensive outpatient, and outpatient) are effective in reducing substance use and criminal activity even in mandated clients (Center for Substance Abuse Treatment, 2005). And, according to the National Institute on Drug Abuse (2014), mandated clients have the same rates of treatment success as non-mandated clients. Do not be pessimistic about a client who has been referred through the criminal justice system. Client ambivalence to change is natural whether they are self-referred or mandated. A collaborative, person-centered approach, like motivational interviewing, can help even resistant clients become more ready to change. Even if your client has not been arrested, charged, or convicted of criminal offenses, your client may have participated in illegal activity. It is important to ask about these behaviors during an assessment. A nonjudgmental approach is important as is an assurance of confidentiality. There are limits to confidentiality, however, and these include situations involving child and elder abuse/neglect and risk of suicide or homicide.

Assessing Substance Use

Obviously, a substance use assessment will include questions about a client's substance use. These questions will include types of substances used, how often, how much, route of administration, last use, and age of first use. Most assessment instruments will include a thorough list of substances for you to ask about. The list should include substances from all classes of drugs and may even include brand names and street names. It is important for you to be aware of some of the more popular street names of drugs; however, names change rapidly, so it is nearly impossible to stay completely up to date on drug slang. If your client mentions a drug by its street name and you are not sure what they mean, do not be afraid to ask. It is worse to assume you know what they are talking about and be wrong than it is to look "uncool."

When asking about specific substances, make sure to give clients examples. For example, do not simply ask "have you ever used any benzodiazepines?" Instead, follow up with a list of examples—"like Valium, Xanax, Klonopin, Ativan, etc.?" Your client may not know that these are known as benzodiazepines and may unintentionally deny use. And be aware that prescription drugs always have a brand name and a generic name. Your client may be using alprazolam (generic name) and not realize it is the same as Xanax (brand name). It is helpful to have a list of commonly used prescription drugs with both generic and brand names handy when doing an assessment. Make sure to ask about each substance listed on the assessment. It may be tempting to save time by asking your client "what substances have you used" and expecting them to name each and every one on their own. Clients may forget or minimize use if you do not ask them directly. Instead, include a thorough list: alcohol, cannabis, hallucinogens, inhalants, PCP, opioids, heroin, sedative/hypnotic/anxiolytics (benzodiazepines), stimulants (including amphetamines, methamphetamine, and cocaine), and other. Do not skip any substance even if your client says "all I've ever used was marijuana and alcohol." And be sure to ask about "other" substances like over-the-counter cold medication (Nyquil, Coricidin, Robitussin). Most of the over-the-counter medications that people get high from contain a substance known as dextromethorphan or DXM. Your client may not recognize the name DXM, but they may have used Coricidin (or triple Cs) to get high. This is especially common in teenagers. Even though DXM is available over the counter, it can have physical, psychological, and withdrawal consequences. Another commonly misused over-the-counter substance is diphenhydramine, found in sleep aids, motion sickness preventatives, and allergy medications. You will want to give specific examples of what you mean by "other substances." All too often counselors get to the end of the list of substances and simply ask "have you used any other substances?" A vague question like this makes it all too easy for a client to say no.

For each substance your client has ever used, you will want to ask more specific questions about their use. Here are the types of questions you will want to ask:

1. At what age did you first use (substance)?
2. When was the last time you used (substance)?
3. During the past 30 days, how many days did you use (substance)?
4. During the past 90 days, how many days did you use (substance)?
5. During the past year, how often did you use (substance)?
6. How much did you use per day (when you used)? Over how many hours?
7. How did you take (substance)? Oral, snorted, smoked, injected?

When you ask a client about their use during the last 30 days, 90 days, or year, it may be helpful to have a calendar with you so you can easily count back to when you are referring. For example, if you are assessing a client in April and you want to know about their use during the last 90 days, you can count back to January. It may be easier for your client to refer to a specific month, like January, than it is to recall the last 90 days.

It is also important to find out if a client has been in a controlled environment during the time frame they report not using. A controlled environment is a place where (theoretically) a client has no access to drugs or alcohol, like jail, a hospital, or a residential rehabilitation facility. A client who has been in jail for the past 90 days and reports being clean and sober the past 90 days is a different situation than a client who has not used while in the community for the past 90 days. You will want to make note of periods of recovery while in a controlled environment in your assessment.

After you have asked about all the substances a client has used, you will want to find out about specific withdrawal symptoms he or she may have experienced, along with prior treatment, support group attendance, criminal charges, and other psychosocial problems he or she may have had related to substance use.

Determining a Diagnosis

A valid and reliable assessment instrument can be used to determine a client diagnosis. These instruments will include questions that align with the DSM criteria for SUDs. For example, an assessment instrument may ask questions such as:

1. Do you currently spend a lot of time using, recovering from the effects of using, or trying to obtain alcohol or drugs?
2. Have you tried to quit or control your use of alcohol or drugs?
3. Have you continued to use despite having persistent or recurrent social or interpersonal problems?
4. Have you continued to use despite having persistent or recurrent physical or psychological problems related to your use?
5. Have you given up or reduced important social, occupational, or recreational activities because of your use?
6. Have you noticed it takes more of the substance to get you high (or intoxicated)?

These are examples of the DSM-5 criteria for SUDs, but rewritten in questions. An assessment instrument with questions like this will aid you in determining if your client meets criteria for a SUD.

Examples of Comprehensive Assessments

The GAIN

Perhaps, one of the most comprehensive biopsychosocial assessment instruments is the Global Appraisal of Individual Needs (GAIN), developed by Chestnut Health Systems. The full GAIN-I is intended to be used as an intake assessment for clients entering treatment. There is training and certification required to use all of the GAIN instruments, but you will likely find it is well worth the time and resources to use the GAIN as your assessment instrument. It is not only valid and reliable, but also incredibly thorough.

The GAIN-I (full version) not only asks about substance use, but also assesses mental health, physical health, educational and vocational issues, criminal justice and legal involvement, risk behaviors, and environment and living situation. There are also follow-up, shortened, and Spanish versions of the GAIN. You can find out more about GAIN instruments at http://gaincc.org (Global Appraisal of Individual Needs Coordinating Center, 2018).

Addiction Severity Index

One of the most widely used comprehensive assessment measures is the Addiction Severity Index (ASI), currently in its 6th version. The ASI was originally developed in the late 1970s by the US Veterans Administration (VA) and focused mainly on assessing males with primarily alcohol and opioid use disorders. Over the years, it has evolved and has been adopted worldwide for use across substance-using populations. The ASI was designed as a medium-structured (also known as semi-structured) instrument. It measures seven areas: medical, employment/finances, alcohol use, drug use, legal, family/social, and psychiatric. The ASI-6 has been shown to be both reliable and valid (Cacciola, Alterman, Habing, & McLellan, 2011). The ASI does require some training to administer, but there is no certification or fee associated with its use.

Summary/Conclusion

Assessment is the foundation on which you build a client's treatment. It is important to use an assessment instrument which is valid, reliable, and comprehensive. Other sources of information can be gathered from previous treatment providers, referral sources, and family interviews to form a more complete assessment of your client. Assessment data will also help determine a diagnosis. As a counselor, you will want to ensure you have adequate training in assessment and that you choose the right instrument.

References

Cacciola, J. S., Alterman, A. I., Habing, B., & McLellan, A. T. (2011). Recent status score for version 6 of the Addiction Severity Index (ASI-6). *Addiction, 106*, 1588–1602.

Capuzzi, D., & Stauffer, M. D. (2008). *Foundations of addiction counseling*. Boston, MA: Pearson Education, Inc.

Center for Substance Abuse Treatment. (2005). *Substance abuse treatment for adults in the criminal justice system*. Treatment Improvement Protocol (TIP) Series 44. DHHS Publication No. (SMA) 05-4056. Rockville, MD: Substance Abuse and Mental Health Services Administration.

Dennis, M. L., White, M., Titus, J. C., & Unsicker, J. (2007). *Global appraisal of individual needs: Trainer's training manual and resources*. Bloomington, IN: Chestnut Health Systems.

Doweiko, H. E. (2012). *Concepts of chemical dependency* (Eighth Edition). Belmont, CA: Brooks/Cole.

Global Appraisal of Individual Needs Coordinating Center. (2018). *GAIN Instruments*. Retrieved from http://gaincc.org

National Institute on Drug Abuse (2014). Principles of Drug Abuse Treatment for Criminal Justice Populations - A Research-Based Guide. Retrieved from https://www.drugabuse.gov/publications/principles-drug-abuse-treatment-criminal-justice-populations-research-based-guide on 2018, June 20.

Substance Abuse and Mental Health Services Administration. (2009). *Integrated treatment for co-occurring disorders: The evidence*. DHHS Pub. No. SMA-08-4366, Rockville, MD: Center for Mental Health Services, Substance Abuse and Mental Health Services Administration, U.S. Department of Health and Human Services.

Chapter 6

Multicultural Considerations with Special Populations

Zach Sneed

Key Terms: multicultural and pluralistic characteristics among diverse groups, biological, neurological, and physiological factors that may present with substance use disorders

Key Objectives: After reading this chapter, students will be able to: a) identify the purpose of attending to culture as a component of the assessment process; b) implement a culturally appropriate SUD screen.

Culture is a construct that many novice counselors struggle to work with. The term involves multiple sets of beliefs, values, customs, and other variables that drive an individual's perception of the world around them. The client's perception involves thoughts, behavior, emotions, and judgments about the person's environment and people within it. In terms of counseling, when counselors practice in a culturally competent manner, clients will be more engaged and more likely to benefit from substance use counseling. Focusing on being culturally competent drives therapeutic decision-making and helps counselors create treatment plans that are more likely to fit their clients. According to the Substance Abuse and Mental Health Services Administration (SAMHSA), culture is a "conceptual system developed by a community to . . . structure the way people view the world" (SAMHSA, 2014, p. 16). Consider culture as adherence to a shared set of norms, beliefs, or values, but be open to the individualized expressions or interpretations of your clients.

In the 1980s, culture was recognized as an important need to attend to in professional counseling (Sue et al., 1982). As the American population continues to diversify, the need for counselors to be prepared to work with a diverse array of clients across the lifespan grows. Current U.S. Census Bureau (2017a) reports indicate that minority group members now represent 38.7% of the population while immigrants are estimated to account for 13.2%. Certainly, counselors need to be prepared to work with individuals from a variety of cultural backgrounds (Sue & Sue, 2013).

The first set of training standards addressing cultural diversity and assessment in counseling was created in 1992, by the Association for Assessment in Counseling (Association for Assessment in Counseling and Education [AACE], 2012). These standards require counselors to incorporate cultural competency and pay close attention to the impact of multicultural factors. What we seek to identify is not only whether our assessment has merit, but also to what degree it is accurate for the current client. Attending to cultural considerations then becomes a particularly individualized and applied process. As such, the results of your assessment reflect your understanding of the current person you are working. Similar to how counselors make a diagnosis that is based on multiple sources of information, multicultural considerations provide additional opportunities to better fit treatment approaches and plans for a client (Jones & Welfare, 2017; SAMHSA, 2014). This chapter will focus specifically on multicultural considerations for substance use disorders (SUDs).

Cultural Competency

Cultural competency is founded on the interconnectedness between a counselor's knowledge base, skills set, and self-awareness (SAMHSA, 2014). Counselor self-awareness refers to the phenomenon of a counselor being not only aware, but also actively vested in exploring his or her own cultural values, assumptions, and beliefs. Self-awareness includes knowledge, beliefs, attitudes, values, and skills (Hays, 2017). One of the first steps to become culturally competent is for counselors to explore their own heritage. Many counseling students and novice counselors struggle with this process, thus mentoring and supervision relationships can be useful. Another facet in becoming culturally competent has to do with the counselor's knowledge base about populations they tend to work with. Counselors should reflect on their attitudes, beliefs, and knowledge about culture and its effect on counseling. Similarly, counselors should continually seek to improve their knowledge base about the groups they work with and take steps to learn about any new groups or cultures the counselor encounters. Cultural competency is both a process and outcome.

Cultural Characteristics

Culture takes many forms and it is possible for a client, or a counselor, to have many cultural group affiliations and referents. There are multiple descriptive terms associated with multiculturalism. Cultural characteristics include the concepts of race, ethnicity, nationality, sex, gender, affectional status, disability status, geography, language, religion, and others. Counselors should take care to be self-aware of their own values and beliefs around all of these characteristics so as to promote the well-being of their clients.

Race and ethnicity are two concepts that are generally confused. Race is often tied to an individual's outward appearance. It is used to physically identify one group of individuals as being different from another. Ethnicity is different from race, in that it is used to identify and describe a group that shares a common identity and heritage. It is possible for people from the same race to have different ethnic backgrounds and vice versa. Additional characteristics that are often confused with race or ethnicity include nationality and language. The term nationality refers to a person's country of origin when used in ancestral terminology, as in a person could be of Spanish descent or birth. Another use of the term is as a current descriptor of national affiliation. People who currently have citizenship status in a country are accurately described as being from that country. So, individuals may have more than one nationality that they identify with.

Language is also viewed as a cultural referent; however, it is also often confused with nationality and race or ethnicity. Language contributes a great deal toward cultural values and beliefs, as it is one of the driving forces of transmitting culture from one generation to the next. Providers should be aware of cultural norms associated with, both, spoken and nonverbal methods of communication. These include personal space and nonverbal cues, verbal displays or messages about emotional or cognitive discomfort, and rules or social traditions about speaking about family issues or personal issues.

Sex and gender are two more terms that are often used interchangeably and are also often confused. Affectional status is a newer descriptor in comparison to the other listed characteristics. It is listed here, separately from gender and sex, to reflect its importance in counseling, and also to a larger extent to society as a whole. In the past, gender, sex, and affection were considered to only exist in one of two ways—male or female. Researchers and the public viewed those two groups as being homogeneous. Biological and social science research has advanced significantly and we better understand the concepts now. Sex is used to describe a person's primary sex characteristics, including anatomy. At a basic level, this determination is based on the person's reproductive system. Gender is a term that continues to evolve and is used to identify and describe social roles, based on the interaction of sex and societal expectations. Gender is much more complicated than sex. Counselors discussing gender should be open to exploring gender roles, norms, identity, and expression. Affectional status, quite simply, refers to an affectional bond that one person has for another.

Groups, or terms, related to affectional status include heterosexual, homosexual, lesbian, gay, bisexual, queer, intersex, questioning, and ally (American Counseling Association [ACA], 2009). The terms associated with this group are continually evolving and counselors should take care to use the appropriate terms.

Disability status is another variable that presents individualized cultural characteristics. Multiple disability groups have cultural referents associated with them as well as the much larger group of all people with disabilities. These will be discussed later in the chapter.

Religion is a cultural consideration counselors should also attend to with clients. Clients present across a spectrum of religions. The five most populous religions in the United States are Christianity, Judaism, Islam, Hindu, and Buddhism (Pew Research Center, 2018) though there are many others. Clients will also display great variability in their adherence to and application of their chosen religious beliefs. Due to the variety of religious doctrines, practices, and theologies, providers would be wise to learn the basic tenets and terminology related to their current client base. One thing to keep in mind is that for many people, religious affiliations and spiritual traditions can be both sources of support and areas of personal struggle. For people working to overcome a SUD, religion or spirituality represents a natural pathway to access hope (Shumway et al., 2014).

Acculturation is the process by which individuals change their native cultural referents and worldview to integrate their current surroundings following immigration. Acculturation occurs, typically, over a long period of time and has generational components to it (SAMHSA, 2014). Traditional views of acculturation liken it to a stage approach where individuals start out as wholly oriented to their native culture and move through transitions to become assimilated. Assimilation refers to the process of persons moving closer to embracing the mainstream, or dominant, culture around them and identifying less with their native culture. Current research now indicates that people are more likely to selectively merge aspects of the family's prior cultural referents with those of the new environment/culture.

Emic and Etic Perspectives

Two related and complementary perspectives on multiculturalism have been proposed. The concepts of emic and etic relate to how one studies and applies learning to a culture. These two approaches are based in anthropology and have been applied to counseling for more than two decades.

In the emic perspective, a culture is studied from within. The focus is on understanding how members of that culture define their worldviews. This can extend to all facets of life, as members of the cultural group see it. Of particular importance is the focus on the cultural group of interest, rather than in comparison with others. Essentially, the emic viewpoint is an internal view of cultural qualities. For counselors, this is a useful approach and allows us to cognitively empathize with an individual and try to see the world as they do. Emic approaches in counseling can focus on communication, meaning, goal-setting, planning, and individual aspects of social construction. The primary goal is to approach and understand a client from his or her point of view. Having the appropriate cultural knowledge then allows a counselor to devise interventions, apply techniques and other counseling practices in a culturally responsible way. This increases the likelihood that the clinical efforts will be culturally appropriate and seen as relevant to the needs of the client.

Conversely, the etic approach seeks to understand a specific culture in comparison with other cultures. The focus tends to be on characteristics that are considered to have a universal quality and are seen as a commonality among all people. Etic counselors believe that mental or behavioral health disorders develop the same way in every society (Sue & Sue, 2013). This approach has practical applications in counseling too. For example, measuring constructs such as intelligence or personality traits can be an appropriate use of an etic perspective in counseling. Other constructs that can be viewed through the etic lens include safety, dignity, shelter, and basic needs. Overall, the etic approach is conceptualized as focusing on cross-cultural constructs.

Culture and Bias

The assessment process is one that has multiple opportunities to encounter multicultural bias. This bias is not intended, but can occur if providers are not committed to being aware of the times and places that bias can influence assessment results. Counselor awareness of culture and the commitment to attend to cultural variables has the potential to diminish the impact of bias in the assessment process.

Test Bias

Testing instruments are prone to potential bias. The Standards for Educational and Psychological Testing were developed and published jointly by the American Educational Research Association (AERA), American Psychological Association (APA), and the National Council on Measurement in Education (NCME). These standards, updated in 2014, have been in place since 1966 and stipulate requirements and guidance, for test developers and users, in the areas of psychometrics, fairness, test development, and applications. Though many test publishers and developers have made strides in developing and refining tests to limit sources of cultural bias, counselors still need to examine for its impact among tests. Test bias can arise in multiple ways, and counselors should look for evidence related to norming, content, language, and reliability and validity of the selected measures.

Counselors need to identify whether the test content and norming groups are appropriate for the test takers. Evidence of this can be found by reviewing the test user's manual or closely reviewing the test developer's publicly available information. If norming data, including validity and reliability statistics, are not available for people from different racial, ethnic, or linguistic backgrounds, the test results should be used cautiously when administered to people who are members of the underrepresented groups. Providers need to interpret findings individually and keep in mind the client's cultural and linguistic characteristics.

Hood and Johnson (2006) recommend that providers ask themselves the following questions about tests prior to use:

- Is there any test material that is controversial or inflammatory to relevant subgroups?
- Is there any test material that is stereotypically demeaning to the relevant subgroup?
- Do the test items give positive representations of the relevant subgroup?
- Are the test items balanced in terms of being equally familiar to all subgroups?
- Is this test going to be useful with the current client, or client base, you are working with?

Counselor Bias

Additional ways bias can be introduced into the assessment process via the test administrator or counselor. For example, if a counselor, or other professional, is unfamiliar with the test procedures, the likelihood of accuracy decreases. Counselors have a responsibility to ensure they are prepared to administer a test or exam. In the event that a counselor is unprepared to administer the exam, they may misinterpret a client statement/response or deviate from a test protocol. This can increase the error variance present in an exam and challenges its validity.

Misunderstandings can occur where the counselor does not understand information, either verbal or nonverbal, conveyed by the client and substitutes erroneous information (Liang, Matheson, & Douglas, 2016). The errant information may be based in a western viewpoint of counseling or have roots in stereotyping or prejudice (Hays, 2017; Hood & Johnson, 2006). These types of errors are referred to as ethnocentric. Similarly, language differences between the client and the counselor can contribute to misunderstandings and misattributions (Sue & Sue, 1990). In some cultures, mental or emotional distress is frequently described as having a physical form or pain, rather than psychologically. This is referred to as somatization and is an emic communication style. A counselor who failed to understand that would miss the chance to identify that the client is struggling with psychological distress.

Clinical judgment issues are among the most damaging cross-cultural errors that can occur in counseling. Errors in judgment will cause a counselor to misdiagnose a person or misinterpret an assessment score or report, due to cultural variables, yielding impactful inaccuracies. These may arise out of deliberate or unintentional processes within the counselor. When a counselor assumes a cultural variable is the cause of a clinically significant dysfunction or negative observation, the counselor is diminishing the utility of the assessment results (Hays, 2017). These judgments affect clinical decision-making and increase the likelihood of misdiagnosis. A misdiagnosis is unhelpful to a client and potentially damaging as it delays or prevents the appropriate treatment (Liang et al., 2016; Malgady, 1996). Further, it creates a history of inaccurate clinical labels that will follow the person and can impact their healthcare, self-esteem, and life goals. Counseling and psychology research has repeatedly identified that members of nondominant cultural groups are more likely to be misdiagnosed (Bart, 2018; Bernstein et al., 2006; Hays, 2017; Hood & Johnson, 2006; Liang et al., 2016; Kress, Eriksen, Rayle, & Ford, 2005; Sue & Sue, 1990, 2013); therefore, it is imperative the counselors examine their clinical decision-making processes for sources of potential bias and take appropriate mitigating steps.

Specific Cultural Groups

African Americans

In the United States, about 13% of the population identifies as African American. Data from the National Survey on Drug Use and Health (NSDUH), in 2014, indicate that rates of alcohol use among African Americans are lower than in the general population. For example, past month alcohol use rate for African Americans was 17.3%, whereas for the general population, it was 22.8%. Binge-drinking rates (21.6%) are also lower for this community compared to the average (23%). Illegal drug use rates are slightly higher than the average though, with African Americans reporting past month use of 12.4% with the general population average of 10.2%.

African Americans tend to have similar needs for counseling as the general population, but have very different treatment outcomes (Sue & Sue, 2013). The history of African Americans is one fraught with oppression. Counselors should pay attention to the intergenerational lessons that have been passed down in African American families and seek to allow the client to assert control where possible. Additionally, the effects of prejudice and discrimination may contribute to clients being less trustful of the assessment process. Many African Americans struggle with underemployment, poverty, and health disparities (Sharma, 2008). Both poverty and difficulties with health insurance create additional barriers to accessing substance use treatment programs. Counselors better serve this community by embracing an emic perspective. Exploring problems from the perspective of the family unit, showing flexibility, and collaboratively choosing assessment processes and strategies can increase client motivation and participation (Hays & Erford, 2014).

American Indians and Alaska Natives

Approximately 1.7% of the U.S. population identifies as American Indians and Alaska Native, roughly 5 million people. Diversity within this group is also important as there are 567, distinct, federally recognized tribes (U.S. Department of the Interior, Bureau of Indian Affairs, 2017.) Though this group is one the smallest racial/ethnic groups, in the United States, it experiences the most significant rates of SUDs

(SAMHSA, 2018). In 2014, past month alcohol use rates were 21.9%, while the national average was 22.8%. The rate of illegal drug use was higher than the U.S. average at 14.9%. Of particular importance is the highest rate of drug-induced death among all ethnic and racial groups, reaching 17.1% in 2010. Also, the co-occurring disorder rate was 8.8% for this group compared to the average of 3.3% (SAMHSA).

American Indians and Alaska Natives are sometimes collectively referred to as Native Americans. These cultural groups also struggle with underemployment and poverty. Families tend to be intergenerational and include kinship arrangements that extend families beyond legal boundaries. Another specific concern with this group regards age, as more than one-third of American Indians and Alaska Natives are under the age of 18 (National Congress of American Indians [NCAI], 2018). Increased occurrence of premature death rates applies to this group as well, with approximately only 5.6% of people living beyond 65 years of age (Hays & Erford, 2014).

Counseling interventions with this population are suited to the emic perspective. Counselors should display respect for the client and the history associated with this group. A key goal is to develop client trust in the process of assessment and in the utility of the assessment results. This group has an extensive history with sacrificing autonomy. American Indians and Alaska Native clients generally desire autonomy in decision-making. Consultative strategies can be helpful in this regard, rather than a counselor-driven assessment or treatment plan. Encourage the client to identify strategies for resolving issues in terms they can appreciate. Also attending to coping mechanisms and seeking to enhance social connections will be of help.

Hispanic Americans

In the United States, more than 57 million people identify as Hispanic or Latino (U.S. Census, 2017b). This group represents one of the fastest growing minority groups in the country. Of particular importance is the fact that this group is made up of many different people, from different places, with multiple ethnicities and nationalities. The thing that ties them together is the shared language of Spanish. Hispanic or Latino Americans are not a homogeneous group. Persons identified as Latino in American come from a wide array of countries on multiple continents.

In terms of alcohol and drug use statistics, the Hispanic American population differs from the general population. Past month illicit drug use (8.9%) is lower than the average (10.2%) while past month alcohol use is higher (24.7% vs. 23%) (SAMHSA, 2018). The rates of co-occurring disorders among Hispanic individuals match the national average.

Families of Hispanic descent tend to be collectivistic, thus the importance of exploring family structures and relations during SUD assessment is paramount (Wong & Longshore, 2008). Interpersonal relationships are also very important in most Latin or Hispanic cultures/groups. Family and friends are expected to be helpful and loyal, thus counselors may need to take a wide lens to identify sources of support for treatment planning. The role and importance of spirituality is also an important assessment consideration for many Hispanic subcultures (Wong & Longshore, 2008). For some in this population group, the act of immigrating leads to extensive grief and loss reactions as they leave family and community behind. Immigration can lead to generational difficulties with acculturation and may create additional stressors that lead to SUDs.

Asian Americans, Native Hawaiians, and Other Pacific Islanders

This group is also sometimes referred to as people of Pacific descent. In total, these groups represent about 19.5 million people (6%), of the U.S. population (U.S. Census, 2017c). Of those 19.5 million people, the majority identify as Asian Americans (5.7%) with the remainder identifying as Native Hawaiians or other Pacific Islanders (0.2%). Similar to the Hispanic and American Indian groups, the concept of within-group diversity also applies. This group is composed of people with heritages across eastern, southern, and southeastern Asia, Hawaii, and other Pacific islands, encompassing a very wide geographic area encompassing more than 40 countries or origin.

Regarding substance use statistics, past month illicit drug use was 4.1% among Asian Americans and 15.6% among Native Hawaiians and other Pacific Islanders (NSDUH, 2014). These rates are both above and below the national average of 10.2%. Past month binge alcohol use, for both subgroups, is less than the national average of 23%, with 14.5% of Asian Americans and 18.3% of Native Hawaiians and other Pacific Islanders reporting.

Asian Americans come from a large number of countries, practicing different faiths and using different languages. For some, this leads to acculturative and intergenerational stresses (Sue & Sue, 2013). Family expectations may not match well with individual goals and the family is often seen as a unit responsible for addressing problems (Chang et al., 2017). Counselors employing an emic approach would then do well in following the client's lead in choosing when and how to integrate strategies related to the family dynamic. Asian Americans tend to perform well in academic and employment compared to other minority groups; however that also presents additional sources of stress (Hays & Erford, 2014). Asian Americans may simultaneously struggle with increased expectations by instructors and employers and experience resentment from peers contributing to the development of SUDs. As a result, many Asian Americans continue to feel confusion—it sometimes appears there is no way to be successful. Interpersonal relationships across the Asian cultures tend to focus on balance in the relationship. Relations are typically nondirective and nonconfrontational. Self-restraint and self-control are expected, and display of strong emotions is seen as a sign of immaturity. Counselors should be cautious with confrontational assessment techniques and instead look for ways to solicit collaborative decision-making with the client (Hays & Erford).

Disability and Assessment

Americans with disabilities represent about 19% of the population or over 56.7 million people (U.S. Census, 2017). Substance use-related disorders affect individuals with disabilities at rates that are typically much greater than those of the general population (Harley, Bishop, & Burris, 2012; Koch, Nelipovich, & Sneed, 2002). It is estimated that roughly 8–15% of people with disabilities also has a coexisting or co-occurring SUD (Health & Human Services, 2010; SAMHSA, 2016). That equates to between 4.5 million and 8 million people. People with disabilities are, compared to the general population, less employed, more likely to be in poverty, and have poorer health outcomes. The addition of a SUD complicates things and presents individual challenges for counselors. Still, with a thoughtful approach and an emic perspective, counselors can assist people with disabilities to achieve recovery.

Coexisting Disabilities

A coexisting disability is the simultaneous occurrence of a substance use disability and a "traditional disability." Traditional disabilities are inclusive of the spectrum of disability in America. Specific disabilities that are associated with higher than expected incidences of SUDs include: spinal cord injuries, traumatic brain injuries, blindness and visual impairments, Deafness and hearing impairments, serious mental illness, learning disabilities, and people living with multiple disabilities (Robertson, Davis, Sneed, Koch, & Boston, 2009; West, Graham, & Cifu, 2009).

When examining the intersection of disability and counseling, there are similar considerations to other groups previously discussed: awareness, knowledge, and skills. To be successful in providing services to a person with a disability, it is important to be aware of ableism. This is the thought process where one erroneously diminishes the value of another based on a perceived disability.

Each disability type can present unique challenges for the assessment process. As a first step, counselors should start by having an open and nonjudgmental discussion with the client about the nature of their impairment. Counselors should also be sure to ask about prior accommodations the person has used that seemed helpful. Counselors should then consider a variety of test or assessment modifications. These modifications are known as accommodations. An accommodation is a tool, strategy, aid, or device that seeks to lessen the impact of a disability. In general, there are two broad types of accommodation categories: physical and programmatic. Physical accommodation concerns focus on access to a physical space. Consider concepts such as parking, doors, ramps, stairs, elevators, navigation aids or signage, office or testing room setup and supplies as physical concerns. Programmatic accommodations include conceptual accommodations, or strategies, that a counselor may employ to support counseling, testing, and treatment functions.

General Test Accommodation Strategies

The next step in selecting and implementing an accommodation would be to consider a list of generalized strategies. Each of these could be applicable in specific scenarios. The following list describes generic accommodation steps:

- Modifying the presentation format: Using an alternative way to present the information can be useful, but is often time-intensive if a counselor has to create materials. Sometimes test publishers will have resources available to accomplish this task.
- Modifying the response format: This strategy could include changing answer sheets or the way answers are recorded.
- Modifying timing: Some people with disabilities will need increased time to complete an assessment. This may be due to the impact of their disability or it may be due to the nature of an accommodation they are using to complete the assessment. Time accommodations are very common, but counselors should ensure that changing the time requirements will not unduly affect the results. Often test user manuals can be good sources of information to address this concern.
- Using an alternate test: There may be occasions when using one test or modifying it becomes either time or resource prohibitive. Similarly, some tests may yield invalid results if their administration protocols or materials are modified. In these situations a counselor should consider using an alternate test that will provide similar information.

Assessment for Individuals with Visual Impairments

People who are blind or have low vision fall within the category of visual impairments. This group is diverse in the level of functional vision. Counselors and providers should be aware of the effects of distracting noise in a testing situation. Many people with visual impairments can easily be distracted by sounds. Another concern relates to orientation to the room. In particular, the counselor should describe the testing environment and setting for the client. Pay attention to the effect of the physical layout of the room on the client. Many times, people inaccurately believe that people with visual impairments are not affected by their environments. Ask the client if the light level is okay or if there are any unusual or distracting sounds and then try to attend to those concerns prior to beginning the assessment. As mentioned previously, people with visual impairments will, typically, need additional time to complete an assessment. If they are using an alternate format of a test, or having the test read aloud by the counselor or another person, and then responding orally, the test will take longer to complete. At the same time, the extra effort to complete a test or assessment places an additional burden on the person with a visual impairment. You may need to arrange for them to have a break from the testing process.

Counselors should inquire about the client's preferred format for any reading materials. If you are using written materials during an assessment, be sure to acquire the preferred medium. Keep in mind that the average person can read about 600 words per minute, but most recordings, for example an electronic book, have playback speeds at around 200 words per minute. Braille readers tend to read at less than 100 words per minute. If you use computer-delivered exams in your counseling practice, ask the client about their use and comfort level with computers and any accommodative software. There are a variety of accommodative devices and software programs that can be installed on a computer, or used via cloud computing; however, each person will have different experiences and expectations regarding assistive software. It may not always be possible to access software or hardware for accommodations.

There are other considerations to attend to when working with people with visual impairments. Important information about the person's visual impairment and relation to his or her SUD can be identified by exploring the pathology of the visual loss. In other words, finding out whether the vision loss was acquired at birth, progressive, or traumatic as well as personal coping and self-accommodation strategies can be useful. Inquire about the individual's substance use preparation routine or patterns. Also inquire about any travel aids the person uses, such as a long cane, dog guide, or GPS device. Read aloud or mention all the things you show or are doing in the room to help keep the client comfortable. This type of information can help you match them to a treatment level and write a better treatment plan.

Assessment of Individuals with Hearing Impairments

Counselors can work with people with hearing impairments in a variety of ways, the first of which is to identify that individual's preferred communication format. People with hearing impairments are very diverse with some having low hearing levels ranging toward Deafness. People may prefer to use hearing aids, read lips, have a sign language interpreter present, or use some other strategy. Be open-minded to their suggestions as it will help build trust in the relationship.

There are also a variety of descriptors of what it means to be Deaf. Typically, deaf with the word not capitalized refers to the physiological loss of hearing. If the word is capitalized, as in Deaf, the speaker or writer is typically referring to Deaf culture. Deaf culture is typically embraced by sign language speakers. Those individuals were likely raised and schooled in environments with other sign language users. Their native language is generally American Sign Language (ASL) and its syntax and use differs from English. ASL speakers may have a difficult time tests written or conducted in English because it is a second language to them. Thus counselors should weigh the benefits of using tools and tests, written in English, with sign language users. In this circumstance it is generally appropriate to involve a third party sign language interpreter and conduct the test in-person.

As a general rule, testing environments should be free from distractions and errant noises. Most people with hearing impairments are still sensitive to sounds. Also, if the client uses a hearing aid or device, it may pick up extraneous noises and distract the person from the assessment process. If the person requests to use a sign language interpreter, identify which style, or language, the person uses. Then contact local agencies that provide those services. American sign language is common, but there are others such as Signed Exact English (SEE) and Pidgin Signed English (PSE) that are prevalent. This process generally needs to be scheduled in advance, thus it is important information to begin working toward this goal early on. Interpreters are credentialed professionals, have confidentiality requirements, and they typically have a monetary cost associated with them; however, lack of funding is never a legitimate reason to ask a client's family member or child to interpret on their behalf. The client may suggest that you use a family member or friend as a low or no-cost interpreter, or as someone they are familiar with, but this is something you should always decline. Family and friends should not have a professional role in the assessment process for counseling. Meet with the interpreter before your assessment date to clarify the nature and meaning of the questions you will ask. SUD terminology can be difficult for some interpreters to work with. Use National Interpreter Certification (NIC) or the Registry of Interpreters for the Deaf (RID) or a state-certified interpreter with appropriate skills level for SUD treatment (Center for Assessment of Sign Language Interpreters, 2018).

Assessment of Individuals with Intellectual Disabilities and Communication Disorders

Individuals with an intellectual disabilities and communication disorders also experience SUDs. These individuals may have deficits in communication, self-care, activities of daily living, social or interpersonal skills, self-direction, health, academics, employment, or leisure activities. If an accurate assessment is not generated, the client is likely to encounter numerous difficulties throughout the treatment process. Counselors can take steps to work with this population and help make a better connection to substance use counseling by taking several specific steps.

Counselors should inquire about the timelines of substance use. Often with this population, early use coincides with adolescence and young adulthood. Information about their social and peer relations during these years may yield useful data regarding their substance use trajectory. At the same time, an accurate family history of drug or alcohol use is important.

A thorough medication history as well as compliance assessment should be conducted. Some individuals with intellectual disabilities take a variety of medications that must be continued or administered on specific routines throughout the day. Another consideration for counselors has to do with the cognitive processing abilities. Counselors may consider breaking components into smaller pieces and reducing the length of a session to reduce cognitive fatigue. Accommodations should be used to match or modify language and reading materials to the examinee's level.

For individuals who have a communication disorder, patience is often helpful to the counselor. Demonstrate acceptance and positive regard for the client as an individual by allowing the client to answer questions and engage in the conversation without interruption. Try to remove any distracting stimuli from the environment, and keep instructions and directions simple. Allowing the client to respond in a variety of ways that work individually is recommended. Consider allowing clients to specify which strategy will work best for them. These strategies can include nodding, pointing, facial expressions, gestures, and differing tones of voice. Repeat or rephrase questions when appropriate and clarify your understanding of their responses through paraphrasing.

Assessment of Individuals with Physical Disabilities

Physical disabilities is an umbrella term used to describe, typically, people with some type of mobility impairment. These impairments may affect movement of any combination of the limbs. The most common type of impairments involves use of the legs. About half of all people in America with a mobility impairment use wheelchairs. People with physical disabilities may require use of canes, walkers, or wheelchairs. Upper body impairments may include limited or no use of the arms and hands. Many of the muscles in the body or only a few can be affected. People with physical disabilities also may experience a variety of other impairments associated with their specific disability. This group includes people with a cerebral palsy, spinal cord injury, traumatic brain injury, muscular disorders, paralysis, amputations, and a wide variety of other health-related disabilities that affect mobility. Estimates of SUDs among this population vary by specific disability type, but range from 20% to 50% compared to the general population (Corrigan, 1995; Heinemann, Doll, Armstrong, & Schnoll, 1991; Robertson et al., 2009).

When conducting assessments with people with physical disabilities, counselors should prepare to be flexible in terms of the physical test environment, test protocols, and accommodation strategies. Examinees may need furniture to be repositioned or, in some cases, an alternate location to be selected for the day of the assessment. Consider the client's route of travel to your facility and remove any barriers or obstructions when possible. As previously mentioned, additional time may be warranted for the assessment process. Careful consideration of the effect of the disability and its interaction with the assessment process and outcome is necessary (Power, 2006).

Assessment of Individuals with Mental Illness

Substance use is frequently seen among people living with a mental illness (Harley et al., 2012; Robertson et al., 2009). This group is also frequently referred to by the terms co-occurring disorders or coexisting disabilities. Typical diagnoses that fit into the category of co-occurring disorders include schizophrenia, bipolar disorder, mood disorders, anxiety disorders, eating disorders, and psychotic disorders. Estimated rates of SUDs among people with mental illness are consistently higher than the general population and range from 15 to 50% (Brown, Ridgely, Pepper, Levine, & Ryglewicz, 1989; Harley et al., 2012; Robertson et al., 2009; West et al., 2009). This group deals with poverty, chronic unemployment, homelessness, and frequent interactions with the criminal justice system.

Counselors conducting SUD assessments with people with co-occurring disorders need to plan their assessment strategy. It is important to recognize that the two disabilities affect each other, and predispose the person to experiencing a relapse for the other disease Symptoms of the mental illness and SUD can both conceal the other disorder's effects on mental and physical health, psychosocial functioning, and daily activities. With this population, after enough time for the typical withdrawal syndrome to pass occurs, isolation and identification of the mental illness become easier; however, people with serious mental illness have increased risks for health consequences during withdrawal. Medically monitored detoxification programs are a safer option for people with co-occurring disorders, as they provide palliative care and can help ease the person into withdrawal. This decreases the likelihood of a significant relapse of the mental illness.

Previous mental health diagnoses or psychiatric histories, including medications, are important to assess. Simultaneously, counselors should inquire about medication adherence, and seek to identify whether the client has current mental health needs and access to prescription medications. Engagement is another area to pay close attention to, as many people with co-occurring disorders, who have sought SUD treatment, have not had their rehabilitation needs met by community and social service agencies. In the past, many agencies had policies or rules that required a person with a mental illness demonstrate sustained sobriety before qualifying for mental health services. Similarly, community and state substance use facilities had policies around the need for stability, or remission, in mental health diagnoses prior to supplying services. This has led many people with co-occurring disorders to either fall between the cracks. In some cases, based on client experiences, people with co-occurring disorders may have developed the perception where they see agencies as unwilling to help. Attending to engagement allows the counselor to identify other agencies that the client is currently engaged with and to include those agencies as partners in the treatment plan.

Veterans and Assessment

Veterans in the United States represent about 23 million people. Veterans return to civilian life with additional challenges compared to the general population. Many veterans have experienced deployments in dangerous settings, for long periods of time, away from family and friends. For veterans exposed to combat, the psychological stressors are even greater. Recent data indicate that veterans experience post-traumatic stress disorder (PTSD), SUDs, depression, traumatic injuries, and physical disabilities at rates far in excess of the general population (SAMHSA, 2016).

Individuals who experience multiple deployments or sustained combat-related injuries have the greatest risk for developing a SUD. Some veterans may turn to alcohol or drug use as a way to cope with stressors and reintegration into civilian life while others may develop a SUD related to medications prescribed to address their injuries and rehabilitation. SAMHSA (2017) reports that about 7% of veterans experience a SUD. Other research indicates variability in the rates. One study, by Toblin, Quartana, Riviere, Walper, and Hoge (2014) investigating chronic pain and opioid use, found that 23.2% of active duty soldiers reported past month opioid use. Of note was that of those reporting opioid use, 44.1% reported no or mild pain and 5.6% reported no pain in the past month. Hoggatt et al. (2015) conducted a systematic literature review of studies on female veterans involving SUDs. The researchers reported findings from 56 studies and rates of SUDs ranging from 3% to 16%. In a separate systematic review, Lan and colleagues (2016) reported the average rates of alcohol use disorders at 32% and drug use disorders at 20%. All of these estimates exceed that of the general population.

Counselors conducting assessments with veterans need to establish trust with the client. Empathy and patience will enhance the quality of the therapeutic relationship and increase the likelihood that the client sees value in in the process. Important areas to assess in the veterans life include their experiences while deployed as well as reintegrating after leaving the service; family issues, including relations with members of the extended family; the importance of military service in identity development; exercise and sleeping habits; and satisfaction with post service employment and recreational activities. An important consideration for counselors is to remain nonjudgmental when working with veterans. Avoid making assumptions about events that are shared with you, and instead ask the client to characterize or describe them in terms of the client's perceived impact on themselves.

AUDIT-C for Veteran Populations

A recommended tool for use among veterans is the Alcohol Use Disorders Identification Test-Consumption (AUDIT-C). The tool was derived from the first three questions of the AUDIT. It is an easy to use, rapid, screening tool that identifies people who are hazardous drinkers. This screen can also be used with no formal training and at no cost. The AUDIT-C is scored on a scale of 0 to 12, where 0 indicates little or no alcohol use. In men, a score of 4 or more is considered positive; in women, a score of 3 or more is considered positive. If all of the points come from question 1, then it is assumed that the examinee is consuming alcohol in a safe manner. Generally, the higher the AUDIT-C score, the more likely it is that the patient's drinking is affecting her/his health and safety.

The AUDIT-C screening questionnaire:

1. How often do you have a drink containing alcohol?
   - Never (0 points)
   - Monthly or less (1 point)
   - Two to four times a month (2 points)
   - Two to three times a week (3 points)
   - Four or more times a week (4 points)
2. How many drinks containing alcohol do you have on a typical day when you are drinking?
   - 1 or 2 (0 points)
   - 3 or 4 (1 point)
   - 5 or 6 (2 points)
   - 7 to 9 (3 points)
   - 10 or more (4 points)

3. How often do you have six or more drinks on one occasion?
   - Never (0 points)
   - Less than monthly (1 point)
   - Monthly (2 points)
   - Weekly (3 points)
   - Daily or almost daily (4 points)

Scoring: Responses are summed for all three questions. Range of scores = 0–12 points

Culture Fair Assessments

Culture Fair Tests

There are a variety of "culture fair" tests. This term refers to the ability of a test or measurement tool to yield equitable results among different groups. Very few tests exist that are truly culture-free, as most tests are written in a specific language; however, there are several tests, related to SUDs, that have been investigated for their ability to be culturally fair to diverse groups (Table 1).

Table 1 Culture-Fair Assessment Tools for Substance Use Disorders

Instrument	Abbreviation	Description	Group Norms Available	Multiple Languages	Multiple Versions/ Lengths
Addiction Severity Index	ASI	Structured instrument assessing the severity of substance use disorders across multiple scales.	Yes	Yes	Yes
Alcohol, Smoking, and Substance Involvement Screening Test	ASSIST	Screening test developed as a culturally neutral tool for use in primary care settings.	Yes	Yes	No
Alcohol Use Disorders Identification Test	AUDIT	Screening test created for use in multinational settings to identify people with hazardous drinking.	Yes	Yes	Yes
Drug Abuse Screening Test	DAST	Self-report instrument that identifies and ranks problems associated with drug use.	NA	Yes	Yes
Drug Use Screening Inventory	DUSI	Structured instrument assessing the severity of substance use disorders across multiple scales.	Yes	Yes	Yes
Rapid Alcohol Problems Screen	RAPS-4	Four question screening test that rapidly identifies problem use.	Yes	Yes	Yes

Source: Zach Sneed.

Summary/Conclusion

In counseling, the impact of and focus on diversity, nonjudgmental attitudes, and approaches is foundational. Multicultural considerations are important facets of a person's life and culture is not something that can be stripped away or ignored. Assessments need to be culturally relevant and take into account the personal and cultural factors that may affect the client's perception of the problem, presentation of symptoms, and relationship with the therapeutic provider.

The cultural identity of the client includes racial and ethnic identities, gender beliefs, sex, language preferences, and other factors. Individuals with immigration experiences within the last several generations also present with unique acculturative circumstances. Each individual client makes choices about the groups he or she identifies as contributing to and being important for his or her cultural identity. Counselors should meet people where they are with an open mind, and a holistic and culturally competent perspective. The main point of assessment is to effectively and accurately identify client strengths, limitations, and perspectives that are necessary to provide an accurate clinical diagnosis and treatment plan.

When a counselor can be open to exploring his or her own cultural history and beliefs, it creates an environment of openness and inclusivity. Self-reflection provides counselors with a tool to promote their own clinical and professional development. As a provider's client base demographics change, counselors can engage, first, through self-reflection, on beliefs, attitudes, and values about a specific group. Then the counselor can actively engage in the process of acquiring new forms of relevant cultural knowledge. Another tool counselors can use to enhance their work knowledge base and assessment efforts with multicultural populations is to engage with clinical supervision. Through the process of supervision, counselors have the opportunity to discuss their own viewpoints, beliefs, and limitations with specific populations. It also represents an active relationship to help guide the counselor toward being better prepared with culturally different groups.

Case Studies

Study 1-Rob:

Rob is a 23-year-old African American male. He is currently engaged and has one child with his fiancé. He lives in a suburban community and was referred to a counselor, via his employer, for what was described as "on the job intoxication." The client says that his employer is concerned about his drug use because he failed a drug test after an accident at work. Rob was suspended for 1 month, pending the outcome of his referral to counseling. Rob tells you that he smokes marijuana, only a few times a week. Additionally, he asserts that he is using cannabis for medicinal reasons, specifically to help with insomnia. Rob reports he does not go to work intoxicated and only smokes marijuana at night to help him sleep. Rob is worried about explaining why he may lose his job to his family. He does not see a problem with his use of marijuana and also states he likes his job, but feels like his boss is just trying to control him. Rob believes that he should be able to use marijuana since it ". . . has never hurt anyone" and is a medicine. Rob says he is willing to participate in counseling ". . . if he has to and it helps him keep his job." The employer has given the client 4 weeks to start.

- What are some of your observations about the case of Rob?
- Are their cultural considerations to attend to?
- How might Rob feel about counseling?
- What steps could you take to get a clearer picture of Rob's case?

Study 2-Berta:

Berta is a 45-year-old Hispanic female who lives in a midsize city. She considers herself very traditional. She has sought the assistance of a counselor at the insistence of her husband for what was described as "excessive drinking." Berta tells the counselor that she began drinking, daily, after the unexpected death of her closest friend, Maria, 6 months ago. Berta and Maria immigrated, together, to the United States 15 years ago. Berta and Maria met their spouses and started their families after immigrating. The client also says that her family is concerned as she has missed work several times due to being intoxicated or being hungover. Berta reports that she rarely feels the urge to attend church since Maria passed away. Berta says that she does not feel her husband or family members are supportive and do not understand what he or she is going through. The client does not see a problem with her use of alcohol, and instead feels that is one of the only things helping her through this terrible time in her life.

- What are your thoughts about Berta?
- What preconceived notions or stereotypes do you have regarding this case?
- What other types of information are needed to be helpful?

Resources

http://www.aera.net/Publications/Books/Standards-for-Educational-Psychological-Testing-2014-Edition-Standards for educational and psychological testing (2014).

https://www.counseling.org/docs/default-source/competencies/multicultural-and-social-justice-counseling-competencies-American Counseling Association (2015). Multicultural and Social Justice Counseling Competencies. Washington, DC.

https://www.healthquality.va.gov/guidelines/MH/sud/-Department of Veterans Affairs (2015). VA/DoD Clinical Practice Guideline for Management of Substance Use Disorders (SUD). Washington, DC.

https://www.integration.samhsa.gov/clinical-practice/screening-tools#drugs–SAMHSA screening instruments

https://www.mentalhealth.va.gov/communityproviders/-Department of Veterans Affairs Community Provider Toolkit (2018).

References

American Counseling Association. (2009). *ALGBTIC competencies for counseling with transgender clients.* Alexandria, VA: Author. Retrieved from: https://www.counseling.org/docs/default-source/competencies/algbtic_competencies.pdf

Association for Assessment in Counseling and Education. (2012). *Standards for multicultural assessment.* Retrieved from http://aarc-counseling.org/assets/cms/uploads/files/AACE-AMCD.pdf

Bart, G. (2018). Ethnic differences in psychosocial factors in methadone maintenance: Hmong versus non-Hmong. *Journal of Ethnicity in Substance Abuse, 17*(2), 108–122. doi:10.1080/15332640.2017.1371656.

Bernstein, J., Bernstein, E., Shepard, D. S., Valentine, A., Heeren, T., Winter, M., . . . Hingson, R. (2006). Racial and ethnic differences in health and health care: Lessons from an inner-city lessons from an inner-city patient population actively using heroin and cocaine. *Journal of Ethnicity in Substance Abuse, 5*(2), 35–50. doi:10.1300/J233v05n02_03

Brown, V. B., Ridgely, M. S., Pepper, B., Levine, I. S., & Ryglewicz, H. (1989). The dual crisis: Mental illness and substance abuse, present and future directions. *American Psychologist, 44*(3), 565–569.

Center for Assessment of Sign Language Interpreters. (2018). Retrieved from: http://www.casli.org/about-casli/

Chang, J. S., Sorensen, J. L., Masson, C. L., Shopshire, M. S., Hoffman, K., McCarty, D., & Iguchi, M. (2017). Structural factors affecting Asians and Pacific Islanders in community-based substance use treatment: Treatment provider perspectives. *Journal of Ethnicity in Substance Abuse, 16*(4), 479–494. doi:10.1080/15332640.2017.1395384

Corrigan, J. D. (1995). Substance abuser as a mediating factor in traumatic brain injury. *Archives of Physical Medicine and Rehabilitation, 76,* 302–309.

Harley, D. A., Bishop, M., & Burris, J. (2012). Persons with disabilities. In D. Capuzzi & D. C. Stauffer (Eds.), *Foundations of addiction counseling* (2nd ed., pp. 301–320). Upper Saddle River, NJ: Pearson.

Hays, D. G. (2017). *Multicultural considerations in assessment* (6th ed.). In D. G. Hays (Ed.), *Assessment in counseling: Procedures and practices* (pp. 67–96). Boston, MA: Pearson.

Hays, D. G., & Erford, B. T. (2014). *Developing multicultural competence: A systems approach.* Boston, MA: Pearson.

Health & Human Services. (2010). HHS, Healthy People 2010.

Heinemann, A., Doll, M., Armstrong, K., & Schnoll, S. (1991). Substance abuse and receipt of treatment by persons with long-term spinal cord injuries. *Archives of Physical Medicine and Rehabilitation, 72,* 482–487.

Hoggatt, K., Jamison, A., Lehavot, K., Cucciare, M., Timko, C., & Simpson, T. (2015). Alcohol and drug misuse, abuse, and dependence in women veterans. *Epidemiologic Reviews, 37*(1), 23–37.

Hood, R., & Johnson, R. (2006). *Assessment in counseling: A guide to the use of psychological assessment procedures* (4th ed.). Alexandria, VA: American Counseling Association.

Jones, C. T., & Welfare, L. E. (2017). Broaching behaviors of licensed professional counselors: A qualitative inquiry. *Journal of Addictions & Offender Counseling, 38*(1), 48–64. doi:10.1002/jaoc.12028

Koch, S., Nelipovich, M., & Sneed, Z. (2002). Alcohol and other drug abuse as coexisting disabilities: Considerations for counselors serving individuals who are blind or visually impaired. *RE:view, 33*(4), 151–159.

Kress, V. E., Eriksen, K. P., Rayle, A. D., & Ford, S. W. (2005). The DSM-IV-TR and culture: Considerations for counselors. *Journal of Counseling & Development, 83*(1), 97–104.

Lan, C., Fiellin, D., Barry, D., Bryant, K., Gordon, A., Edelman, E., . . . Marshall, B. (2016). The epidemiology of substance use disorders in US Veterans: A systematic review and analysis of assessment methods. *American Journal on Addictions, 25*(1), 7–24.

Liang, J., Matheson, B. E., & Douglas, J. M. (2016). Mental health diagnostic considerations in racial/ethnic minority youth. *Journal of Child and Family Studies, 25*(6), 1926–1940. http://doi.org/10.1007/s10826-015-0351-z

Malgady, R. G. (1996). The question of cultural bias in assessment and diagnosis of ethnic minority clients: Let's reject the null hypothesis. *Professional Psychology: Research and Practice, 27*(1), 73–77. doi:10.1037/0735-7028.27.1.73

National Congress of American Indians. (2018). *Demographics.* Retrieved from: http://www.ncai.org/about-tribes/demographics

Office of the Surgeon General (US); Center for Mental Health Services (US); National Institute of Mental Health (US). Rockville (MD): Substance Abuse and Mental Health Services Administration, August, 2001.

Pew Research Center. (2018). *Religious landscape study.* Retrieved from: http://www.pewforum.org/religious-landscape-study/

Power, P. W. (2006). *A guide to vocational assessment* (4th ed.). Austin, TX: Pro-Ed.

Robertson, S. L., Davis, S. J., Sneed, Z., Koch, D. S., & Boston, Q. (2009). Competency issues for alcohol/other drug abuse counselors. *Alcoholism Treatment Quarterly, 27*(3), 265–279. doi: 10.1080/07347320903014347

Sharma, M. (2008). Substance abuse in minorities. *Journal of Alcohol and Drug Education, 52*, 3–8.

Shumway, S. T., Dakin, J. B., Smock Jordan, S. A., Kimball, T. G., Harris, K. S., & Bradshaw, S. D. (2014). The development of the hope and coping in recovery measure (HCRM). *Journal of Groups in Addiction & Recovery, 9*(4), 280–293. doi:10.1080/1556035X.2014.969059

Substance Abuse and Mental Health Services Administration. (2014). *Improving cultural competence. Treatment Improvement Protocol (TIP) Series No. 59* (HHS Publication No. (SMA) 14-4849). Rockville, MD: Author.

Substance Abuse and Mental Health Services Administration. (2016). *Co-occurring disorders.* Retrieved from https://www.samhsa.gov/disorders/co-occurring

Substance Abuse and Mental Health Services Administration. (2017). *Veterans and military families.* Retrieved from: https://www.samhsa.gov/veterans-military-families

Substance Abuse and Mental Health Services Administration. (2018). *Racial and ethnic minority populations.* Retrieved from https://www.samhsa.gov/specific-populations/racial-ethnic-minority

Sue, D. W., Bernier, J. E., Durran, A., Feinberg, L., Pedersen, P., Smith, E. J., & Vasquez Nuttall, E. (1982). Position paper: Cross-cultural counseling competencies. *The Counseling Psychology, 10*, 45–52.

Sue, D. W., & Sue, D. (1990). *Counseling the culturally different: Theory & practice* (2nd ed.). New York, NY: John Wiley.

Sue, D. W., & Sue, D. (2013). *Counseling the culturally diverse: Theory & practice* (6th ed.). New York, NY: John Wiley.

Toblin, R. L., Quartana, P. J., Riviere, L. A., Walper, K. C., & Hoge, C. W. (2014). Chronic pain and opioid use in US soldiers after combat deployment. *JAMA Internal Medicine, 174*(8), 1400–1401. doi:10.1001/jamainternmed.2014.2726

U.S. Census Bureau. (2017a). Facts for features: Anniversary of Americans with Disabilities Act: July 26 (Census Bureau Publication No. CB17-FF.11): Retrieved from https://www.census.gov/newsroom/facts-for-features/2017/cb17-ff11-disabilities.html

U.S. Census Bureau. (2017b). Facts for features: Hispanic Heritage Month 2017: August 31 (Census Bureau Publication No. CB17-FF.17): Retrieved from https://www.census.gov/newsroom/facts-for-features/2017/hispanic-heritage.html

U.S. Census Bureau. (2017c). Population estimates. Retrieved from: https://www.census.gov/quickfacts/fact/table/US/PST045217#viewtop

West, S. L., Graham, C. W., & Cifu, D. X. (2009). Rates of alcohol/other drug treatment denials to persons with physical disabilities: Accessibility concerns. *Alcoholism Treatment Quarterly, 27*(3), 305–316. doi: 10.1080/07347320903008190

Wong, E. C., & Longshore, D. (2008). Ethnic identity, spirituality, and self-efficacy influences on treatment outcomes among Hispanic American methadone maintenance clients. *Journal of Ethnicity in Substance Abuse, 7*(3), 328–340. doi:10.1080/15332640802313478

Chapter 7

Assessing Level of Care

Matthew E. Sprong

Lucy Parker

Key Terms: ASAM treatment criteria, stages of change, level of care

Key Objectives: Students will understand the process of assessing the appropriate level of care for an individual with substance-related barriers.

There have been several identified causes that contribute to why an individual continues to use substances despite negative consequences [e.g., genetics, cultural, social influences] (Brooks & McHenry, 2015; Mays, Jones, Delany-Brumsey, Coles, & Cochran, 2017). The Moral Model, Social Learning Model, and the Disease Model are the primary models that have been used to explain why people use drugs and/or alcohol (Rutten, Broekman, van den Brink, & Schippers, 2017). The moral model places blame on the individual and emphasizes that people choose to use substance and with willpower, will be able to refrain from using substances. The social learning model emphasizes that something in the environment is causing a person to use substances. The disease model emphasizes that addiction is a disease that cannot be cured, but it able to be treated. Each model has varying levels of attached stigma associated with it, but scholars are now considering that all three models might be present (biopsychosocial model). Given the fact that there are several factors that contribute to substance-related disorders, several components are considered when determining what type of treatment will be most effective for the client.

During the intake interview, a counseling professional will obtain information related to the history of the present episode, family history, developmental history (e.g., developmental milestones for adolescents), personal/social history (e.g., school or work history, peer relationships), legal history, psychiatric history, medical history, spiritual history, and possibly a mental status examination. This information is vital as a counseling professional who is assessing for a possible substance-related disorder will need to provide evidence to support a diagnosis. In addition to possible diagnosis, the counseling professional is assessing for an (1) inability to consistently abstain from drugs or alcohol, (2) impairment in behavioral control, (3) craving or increased hunger for drugs or rewarding experiences, (4) diminished recognition of significant problems with one's behaviors and interpersonal relationships, and (5) dysfunctional emotional responses (Mee-Lee, 2013). The combination of assessing these above categories in additions with the six dimensions established by the American Society of Addictive Medicine (ASAM) that will be discussed below is important when recognizing the appropriate intervention that will be needed to assist a client in eliminating his or her substance use. The purpose of this chapter is to provide more information related to properly assessing an individual to determine where placement should be made.

Stages of Change Influencing Diagnosis and Treatment

Assessing an individual's current stage of change provides information to a counseling professional in terms of how much treatment and the type of treatment that might be needed for an individual. For example, a person who enters substance use treatment because he or she is mandated by a drug court system will likely have different perceptions related to treatment than an individual who enters treatment at his or her discretion. Obviously, this might not be the case in all instances but an individual who takes initiative and action by themselves is likely to be successful. The stages of change were developed and used in addiction counseling as a way to determine what interventions will likely need to be employed to assist a client in meeting their treatment goals. These stages of change include (1) precontemplation, (2) contemplation, (3) preparation, (4) action, (5) maintenance, and (6) relapse (Prochaska & DiClemente, 1986; Prochaska, DiClemente, & Norcross, 1992). When working with a client and documenting progress and change, a counseling professional must be aware that these stages are not necessarily linear in nature (follow each stage in order), but rather the stages may be repeated in a random order (Rutten et al., 2017). For example, if an individual has spent 3 years in the maintenance phase and suddenly relapses, the client does not automatically go back to stage 1 in terms of their willingness to change.

The *precontemplation* stage involves an individual who does not recognize that his or her behaviors (drinking/drugs) are problematic and therefore no change is needed. Oftentimes a client who is mandated to attend treatment will not completely understand that their continued drug and/or alcohol use is creating additional problems that could be reduced or eliminated if the substance use was significantly decreased or eliminated.

Case Study: Dave is a 52-year-old white male, who is currently employed as a plumber. He has two daughters and is recently divorced from his wife of 25 year. His children are ages 13 and 16. Approximately 10 years ago, Dave was in a 5-year apprenticeship program where he must obtain several thousand hours working under the supervision of a Licensed Plumber in the Union. Dave decided to work for his father's company and was paid cash, so that his father could avoid paying taxes since much of the business involved being paid in cash. After 5 years, Dave was required to submit documentation of his hours. Consequently, Dave was unable to provide documentation as Dave's father did not keep any records in case he was audited, and Dave did not file taxes on earned income because he was paid in cash. Needless to say, Dave was unable to obtain his license despite passing the required examination and completing the required hours of training. As a result of this unfortunate news, Dave started drinking very heavily. Prior to the divorce, Dave and his wife met with a marriage counselor in hopes of salvaging their marriage. Dave's wife complained that Dave was always intoxicated and would often times need to be picked up in the middle of the night. The marriage counselor asked Dave if he thought his drinking was a problem and Dave said no. The next question the marriage counselor asked Dave was if he wanted to stay married. He said yes but was not going to quit drinking. Dave's wife then filed for divorce. Since his divorce, Dave has endured several problems that have resulted in an increase in drinking (drinking until intoxication in the morning, drives home intoxicated, and goes back to the bar once he wakes up sober). He borrowed a bass guitar from a fellow musician and pawned it for alcohol money. The fellow musician and his friends confronted Dave in the alley outside of a bar and proceeded to punch Dave until he was unconscious. Dave had several medical complications because of the fistfight. The people were arrested as another customer of the bar saw the events unfolding and contacted the police department. Dave hired an attorney for assistance with medical bills and his lawsuit was pending until he completed all necessary treatment for his broken rib, broken mandible (jaw), and other issues. A few months later, Dave was arrested on a driving under the influence (DUI) charge. He decided to stop his current medical treatment and settle his case so he could pay the fees associated with his DUI charge.

As evident in the case study above, Dave wants to continue to drink but does not recognize the issues that his drinking is creating. His wife filed for divorce, Dave was involved in a serious fistfight because he pawned a fellow musician's bass guitar for alcohol money and had to settle his case early despite needing additional medical treatment. Dave does not recognize that his daily alcohol use is influencing several parts of his life.

The *contemplation stage* involves an individual who recognizes a problem and is contemplating a change but has not yet committed to changing. This individual is in a state of ambivalence about making the change and teeter-totters on the idea of whether the problem is severe enough to make a change. In the scenario above, Dave was drowning in his alcohol addiction. Despite severe negative consequences, he would continue to drink on a daily basis. If Dave awoke one day and started to realize that his life is falling apart and the drinking is making things worse, he is starting to move from the precontemplation stage to the contemplation stage.

The *preparation stage* involves an individual who is now in the process of preparing to seek out ways to change their unwanted behaviors. For example, an individual might research possible treatment programs of locate support services (e.g., Alcoholics Anonymous, Narcotics Anonymous) available within a local community. However, the phrase "actions speak louder than words" comes into play when involved with an individual who uses substances. The individual may plan to attend counseling for treatment. However, the *action stage* is the next stage that involves an individual who actually puts into place what they have been previously planning.

After a person completes treatment successfully, they may be in the *maintenance stage*, which involves the process of maintaining sobriety. After a person completes treatment, they may need support services to assist in continuing to be substance use free. As will become evident later in the chapter, the level of care a person is assigned to might determine what supports will be needed when a person leaves treatment to assist in maintaining sobriety. For example, a person who was receiving treatment from an inpatient facility might need outpatient services to assist with any obstacles that arise once the client is back at home.

Relapse is the final stage of the stages of change model and is when a person resumes the previous unwanted behavior (e.g., drug use). For example, when individuals attend Alcoholics Anonymous, they receive tokens/coins that represent how many days/months/years that they have been sober. This is an example of the maintenance phase of recovery and if a person were to use alcohol, this would constitute a relapse. The longer a person is in the maintenance phase, the more detrimental the relapse might be. However, an individual who relapses does not imply that all is ruined. There may be obstacles that the individual did not consider that need to be addressed in treatment.

ASAM Placement Criteria: Multidimensional Assessment

In addition to addiction being multidimensional and occurring in stages, the American Society of Addiction Medicine (ASAM) defines addiction as biopsychological (Drymalski, & Nunley, 2017), which is defined in part as a chronic neurological disorder involving many brain functions, most notably a devastating imbalance in the "reward circuitry" (Brooks & McHenry, 2015; Lewis, 2012). ASAM elaborates that one or more fundamental impairments exist in the pleasure center of the brain of someone with an addiction and with this, they are genetically prone to chase the chemical highs produced by their substances or processes (Drymalski, & Nunley). *Addiction* is defined as the use of and self-proclaimed powerlessness to substances regardless of negative or adverse consequences (Goodman, 1990). Addiction was also characterized as having a psychological and behavioral component, and often leads to psychological and physical dependence (American Psychiatric Association, 2013; Center for Behavioral Wellness, 2016). Although somewhat differentiated from this definition, assessment instruments that counseling professionals use include the Diagnostic and Statistical Manual of Mental Disorders (*DSM-5*) and the International Classification of Disease (ICD-10) also define addiction similarly (Saunders, 2017; World Health Organization, 1992). Factors that influence the continuum of an individual's substance use to be categorized from use, abuse, to addiction include: 1) physiological functioning of user, 2) psychological state of user, and 3) sociocultural environment in which the drug is used (American Psychiatric Association, 2013; Mays et al., 2017).

Six dimensions are considered when evaluating the appropriate level of care for an individual that presents substance use barriers. It is important to accurately assess the appropriate level of care because it could become harmful if an individual is not placed correctly. The six dimensions of ASAM placement criteria include (Drymalski & Nunley, 2017):

1. Acute Intoxication and/or Withdrawal potential
2. Biomedical Conditions and Complications
3. Emotional/Behavioral/Cognitive Conditions and Complications
4. Readiness to Change
5. Relapse/Continued Use/Continued Problem Potential
6. Recovery Environment

As discussed in Chapter 3, the goal of a counseling professional is to ascertain information (e.g., direct observation, medical/psychological records, psychological testing) that can assist us in identifying the types of treatment and interventions that will be most beneficial.

Acute Intoxication and/or Withdrawal involves exploring an individual's past and current experiences of substance use and withdrawal. A counseling professional assessing the need for stabilization of acute intoxication, serious withdrawal symptoms both currently and historically, and life-threatening symptoms or seizures during withdrawal (Mee-Lee, 2013). Further assessment related to whether a client has supports to assist in ambulatory detoxification if it is medically safe would be required. Some questions we might ask Dave if we were assessing the appropriate level of care include:

- Will Dave need intoxication management services needed to address acute intoxication?
- Is Dave at risk of severe withdrawal symptoms, seizures, or other medical complications based on his withdrawal history, as well as the amount, frequency, chronicity, and recency of discontinuation of his alcohol consumption?
- Is Dave currently having similar withdrawal symptoms?
- Does Dave have supports to assist in ambulatory detoxification if medically safe?

In examining the case study above, we do not have enough information related to withdrawal symptoms. Some examples of withdrawal symptoms that Dave may experience include anxiety, shaky hands, headache, nausea, vomiting, insomnia, and sweating. This information would need to be obtained from Dave to further assess his level of intoxication or withdrawal. However, from the case study description, we know Dave is drinking very often (twice per day) and is able to drink several beers in one sitting (increased tolerance).

Biomedical Conditions and Complications involves exploring an individual's health history and current physical condition. This would involve ascertaining if the client has any severe physical health problems, whether the conditions are stabilized or actively being addressed/medically monitored, or are there any other chronic conditions that would affect treatment. If the client is unable to function and safely care for themselves, or is unable to manage activities of daily living, they would likely need inpatient services or to be monitored in some capacity to prevent harm to themselves. If we were assessing Dave, we might ask the following questions:

- Does Dave have any current severe physical health problems, or current physical illnesses that need to be addressed due to his risk or potential for treatment complications?
- Are the conditions or complications stabilized, being actively addressed, and being medically monitored?
- Are there chronic conditions that affect treatment?
- Is Dave unable to function and safely care for self?
- Is Dave able to manage the activities of daily living?

It is apparent that Dave has some physical health problems related to the fight he was involved in as he was receiving medical care for injuries. We do not know the extent of these issues but we know he was under current medical treatment until he needed money to pay off a DUI. Dave appears to have issues with not obtaining licensure as a plumber and this will likely need to be addressed in treatment. We are not aware of any psychiatric disabilities or problems that could complicate treatment. For instance, if Dave had a serious psychiatric disability, it is likely that he will need treatment for this as well.

Emotional, Behavioral, or Cognitive Conditions and Complications involve exploring an individual's thoughts, emotions, and psychiatric issues. This might include assessing for any imminent danger of the client harming himself or herself, or someone else. Additionally, we are interested in exploring the ability to function and safely care for themselves, and if there are any current psychiatric-related barriers that complicate treatment or can create risk. If the client is unable to cope with any emotional, behavioral, or cognitive problems, they may need additional attention and services need to be more frequent. Some questions we might ask Dave include:

- Is Dave in imminent danger of harming himself or herself or someone else?
- Can Dave function and safely care for himself?
- Are there current psychiatric barriers or psychological, behavioral, emotional, or cognitive complications that need to be addressed because they create risk or complicate treatment?
- Can Dave cope with any emotional, behavioral, or cognitive problems?
- Does his emotional, behavioral, or cognitive problems appear to be caused by the substances?

Dave was arrested for driving under the influence of alcohol and continues to drive while intoxicated between his morning and afternoon/evening drinking routines. This could be considered as an imminent danger of harming himself or someone else. It also appears that Dave is using alcohol to cope with problems he is experiencing in his life.

Readiness to Change involves exploring an individual's readiness and interest in changing their drinking and/or drug behavior. As discussed above, there are six stages of change (i.e., precontemplation, contemplation, preparation, action, maintenance, and relapse) and identifying the correct stage of change will be beneficial in terms of placement into appropriate level of care. A counseling professional would be interested in learning about the client's emotional and cognitive awareness of the need to change, whether the client feels coerced into treatment or is actively objecting to receive treatment, and client ambivalent to treatment. Below are some questions we might pose to Dave if we were his counseling professional:

- What is Dave's emotional and cognitive awareness of the need to change?
- Does Dave feel coerced into treatment or actively object to receiving treatment?

- What is Dave's level of commitment to change?
- Does Dave appear to need substance use treatment/recovery, but is ambivalent or feels it is unnecessary?
- How aware is Dave of the relationship between his alcohol use in the pathological pursuit of reward or relief of negative life consequences?

Based on the questions above, what stage would be closely aligned with Dave's behavior? He mentioned that he does not need counseling and he does not have awareness of the danger of driving under the influence. He has a history of motor vehicle accidents, missing work, family-related challenges, and legal trouble.

Relapse, Continued Use, or Continued Problem Potential involves exploring an individual's unique relationship with relapse or continued use or problems. A counseling professional would be interested in assessing whether the client is in imminent danger of continued severe mental health distress, alcohol use, or drug use. Additionally, assessing if the client has any recognition, understanding, or skills in coping with the addiction or psychiatric disability in order to prevent relapse will be beneficial in determining if the client needs significant intervention. If the client is not receiving the appropriate intervention or level of care, the client may not have the ability to remain abstinent, or gain the skills needed to cope with cravings to use and other relapse triggers. An example of a question we might pose to Dave is "Are you likely to continue the use of alcohol in an immediately danger manner?" If Dave's response is no, this confirms that he might not consider drinking under the influence as an immediate danger. If Dave responds yes, then this is problematic as he knows he is causing immediate danger while drinking.

The *Recovery Environment* is the final dimension in determining appropriate level of care. This involves assessing an individual's living environment or situation, and the surrounding people, places, and things associated with this living situation. For example, if an individual was living with his best friend who also has an addiction to substances, this would not be an appropriate place to assist in the recovery process as there may be several triggers that increase the likelihood of using substances. A counseling professional is exploring if there are any dangerous family, significant others, living/working situations threatening a person's safety, immediate well-being, and/or sobriety. In Dave's situation, it appears his sisters want him to stop drinking alcohol and will be able to provide positive support. However, it is always important to ask the client for their perception into this issue. What if Dave mentions that his sisters always come home intoxicated as well? Remember, there are several methods we should incorporate to gather information before making decisions and/or conclusions to treatment.

Risk Rating and Level(s) of Care

The ASAM created a risk rating scale to be used in each dimension as a means to provide numerical values to assess the severity of each dimension. The purpose of the risk scale is to assist a counseling professional in determining what level of care is most appropriate for the individual with the substance use problem, so that the most appropriate treatment(s) and intervention(s) can be provided. As shown below, lower scores would indicate low risk or no issue present, and higher scores would indicate greater risk (Mee-Lee, 2013).

1. This rating would indicate a nonissue or very low-risk issue. The patient would present no current risk and any chronic issues would be mostly or entirely stabilized.
2. This rating would indicate a mildly difficulty issue, or present minor signs and symptoms. Any existing chronic issues or problems would be able to be resolved in a short period of time.
3. This rating would indicate moderate difficulty in functioning. However, even with moderate impairment, or somewhat persistent chronic issues, relevant skills or support systems may be present.

4. This rating would indicate a serious issue or difficulty coping within a given dimension. A patient presenting at this level of risk may be considered in or near "imminent danger."
5. This rating would indicate issues of utmost severity. The patient would present with critical impairments in coping and functioning, with signs and symptoms, indicating an "imminent danger" concern.

The six dimensions provide a structure for a timely and comprehensive review of any life area that could be impacted by the substance use and/or other physical or psychological problems. However, ASAM suggests providing an immediate need profile (either in person or by phone) to assess whether there is acute need for immediate service. Within the ASAM manual, there are specific questions that should be asked of each individual. An imminent danger scale is also included in the manual and there are three options for assessing immediate danger:

A. A strong probability that certain behaviors (such as continued alcohol, other drug use or addictive behavior relapse) will occur.
B. The likelihood that such behaviors will present a significant risk of serious adverse consequences to the individual and/or others (as in reckless driving while intoxicated, or neglect of a child).
C. The likelihood that such adverse events will occur in the very near future, within hours and days, rather than weeks or months.

The counseling professional should ascertain all of the above information and then complete an immediate need profile that helps identify what level of care will be most beneficial to the client. If a client is currently having severe, life-threatening, and/or similar withdrawal symptoms (Dimension 1), current severe physical health problems [e.g., bleeding from mouth or rectum in past 24 hours, recent hypertension; severe pain in chest, abdomen, head] (Dimension 2), and/or is in imminent danger of harming self or someone else or unable to function in activities of daily living or care for self with imminent, dangerous consequences (Dimension 3), then the client is in need to immediately receive medical or psychiatric care for evaluation of need for acute, inpatient care. Chapter 4 of the ASAM criteria provides a detailed evaluation tool to assess the appropriate risk level that is used in determining the appropriate level of care.

Levels of Care

There are five primary levels of care for treatment of substance use that are outlined by the ASAM. The levels of treatment include early intervention (.5), outpatient services (1.0), intensive outpatient/partial hospitalization services (2.0), residential treatment (3.0), and medically managed inpatient services (4.0). Level 2 and Level 3 treatment categories have sub-treatment options that meet specific needs of clients. There are 10 specific levels of care when consider the primary and secondary categories combined (see Table 1).

Early intervention (Level 0.5) involves assessment and education for at-risk individuals who do not meet diagnostic criteria for substance-related disorders. Oftentimes, early intervention is when an individual is driving under the influence of alcohol or substances (e.g., marijuana) and will need risk-education courses that highlight the issues that can occur if continued use in an inappropriate manner is continued. Content may be similar to programs used in schools to educate children about the risks associated with drug usage (e.g., DARE). For example, students who violate the drug or alcohol policy are mandated to participate in a remedial program such as e-CHUG or e-Toke by the judicial system or the school's student code of conduct (Ringwalt, Paschall, & Gitelman, 2011). There is some discussion within the literature related to the efficacy of such early intervention programs (e.g., Belenko et al., 2017; Center for Behavioral Wellness, 2016; Maclean & Saloner, 2017).

Table 1 Level of Care and the Duration/Frequency of Treatment

Level*	ASAM Level of Care	Duration/Frequency of Treatment
.5	Early Intervention	Assessment and Education for at-risk individuals
1	Outpatient Services	Less than 9 hours of service/week
2.1	Intensive Outpatient	9 or more hours of service/week for treating multidimensional instability
2.5	Partial Hospitalization	20 or more hours of service/week for multidimensional instability not requiring 24-hour care
3.1	Clinical-Managed Low-Intensity Residential	24-hour structure with available trained professional; at least 5 hours of clinical service/week
3.3	Clinical-Managed Med-Intensity Residential	24-hour care with training counselors to stabilize multidimensional imminent danger. Less intense milieu and group treatment for those with cognitive or other impairments unable to use full active milieu or therapeutic community
3.5	Clinical-Managed High-Intensity Residential	24-hour care with trained counselors to stabilize imminent danger and prepare for outpatient services
3.7	Medically Monitored Intensive Inpatient	24-hour nursing care with physician availability for significant problems in Dimension(s) 1, 2, or 3. Sixteen hour/day counselor availability
4	Medically Monitored Intensive Inpatient	24-hour nursing care and daily physician care for severe, unstable problems in Dimensions 1, 2, or 3. Counseling available to engage client in treatment

From The ASAM Criteria: Treatment Criteria for Addictive, Substance-Related and Co-Occurring Conditions, Third Edition by American Society of Addiction Medicine. Copyright © 2013 by American Society of Addiction Medicine, Inc. Reprinted by permission.

Outpatient services (Level 1.0) involve less than 9 hours of counseling per week for adults and less than 6 hours per week for adolescents for recovery or motivational enhancement therapies/strategies. Clients continue to work or live within the community but engage in weekly individual and/or group counseling sessions to assist in the obtainment of treatment goals. Specifically, counseling professionals as liaisons between clients' community, workplace, and criminal justice systems to foster societal rehabilitation (Jordan & Andersen, 2017). For example, though abstinence is the majority focus in the United States, many national systems within the United States and surrounding countries are using harm-reduction and rehabilitation strategies alongside outpatient counseling for clients with usage issues. A patient in an ASAM Level 1 program has low dimensional risks across the six ASAM dimensions.

Intensive Outpatient Treatment to Partial Hospitalization (Level 2.0) is similar to outpatient services but involves more direct counseling services. Specifically, adults are required to attend nine or more hours per week, while adolescents are required to attend six or more hours per week. As shown in Figure 1, there are subcategories for different types of services provided within Level 2.0. This includes intensive outpatient services (2.1) and partial hospitalization (2.5). Partial hospitalization involves 20 or more hours of service per week for multidimensional instability not requiring 24-hour care. Similarities may

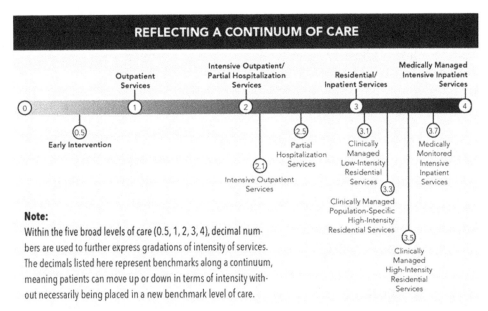

Figure 1. Continuum of Care Established by the American Society of Addiction Medicine.
Source: Mee-Lee (2013).

include employment allowance, community connections, drug court, group therapy, psychoeducation, and counseling interventions (e.g., including both individual and group). Distinguishing factors for intensive outpatient and partial hospitalization programs include added hours required for participation in one's treatment, added monitoring, medication management, mental health services, and potential detoxification and safety monitoring of the client (Welsh et al., 2017).

Residential/Inpatient treatment services has four secondary levels that are designed to provide 24-hour structure with trained professionals. These services are clinically managed and increase in intensity depending on need. For example, clinically managed low residential services (Level 3.1) has the 24-structure but involves a minimum of 5 hours per week of clinical services per week, whereas clinically managed specific high-intensity residential services (Level 3.3) is staffed with 24-hour care but has trained counselors to stabilize multidimensional imminent danger but has less intense milieu and group treatment for those with cognitive or other impairments who are unable to use full active milieu or therapeutic community treatment. Clinically managed high-intensity residential services (Level 3.5) is 24-hour care with trained counselors to stabilize multidimensional imminent danger and prepare for outpatient treatment but the clients are able to use full active milieu or therapeutic community treatment services (Level 3.3. is for clients with specific disabilities that need accommodated treatment services). Medically monitored intensive inpatient services (Level 3.7) involves 24-hour nursing care with physician availability for significant problems in Dimensions 1, 2, or 3. Counseling professionals are available for 16 hours per day. Distinguishing features include added staff such as physicians, psychiatrists, counselors, social workers, case managers, intake counselors, psychologists, peer advocates, and other helpers to assist clients who are usually at a medical or surgical hospital or in psychiatric care. Clients are required to stay in treatment and usually are guided with program regulated and structured days. Family and friends may come during various visiting hours and employment is usually a goal after inpatient treatment. Added structure and regulation is needed for higher level clients as these individuals may face withdrawal problems, and increased co-occurring needs

(Jordan & Andersen, 2017). Though different, inpatient treatment can still be very efficacious and lead to outpatient treatment or even autonomous abstinence. Goals for this care include individualized and cohort-based treatment. Clients may be discharged and usually later attend halfway house and/or choice of residence as regulated by counseling professionals, legal monitors, and advocates. *Medically Managed Intensive Inpatient Services* (Level 4) involve 24-hour nursing care and daily physician care for severe, unstable problems in Dimensions 1, 2, or 3. Counseling is available to engage the client in treatment. The difference between Level(s) 3.2, 3.7, and 4.0 includes:

- Level 3.2: Moderate withdrawal but needs 24-hour support to complete withdrawal management and increase likelihood of continuing treatment or recovery.
- Level 3.7: Severe withdrawal and needs 24-hour nursing care and physician visits as necessary and the client is unlikely to complete withdrawal management without medical and nursing monitoring.
- Level 4.0: Severe, unstable withdrawal and needs 24-hour nursing care and daily physician visits to modify withdrawal management regimen and manage medical instability.

Treatment Level Transitions

When considering clients and their levels of treatment, it is important to remember that client's may transition to varying levels based on factors including if a client is making progress but has not yet achieved goals articulated in their individualized treatment plan (Butler et al., 2008). In other words, continued treatment at a client's present level of care is necessary to permit them to continue to work toward his or her treatment goals, unless they are not yet making progress but have the capacity to resolve their problems with a lesser level of care. When new problems are identified, such as interpersonal stressors, legal issues, or co-occurring mental disorders, clients may be encouraged to find increased levels of care.

Chapter Summary

This chapter featured much information about the stages, types, dimensions, and levels of substance abuse and addiction as well as substance abuse and addiction treatment. When considering this information, it is important for counseling professionals to not be overwhelmed by the different treatment options and to remember that multimodal approaches are best. For counseling professionals to most effectively help clients experiencing substance abuse and/or addiction, it is also important to co-construct therapeutic treatment with the clients themselves, to add client volition and incentive to treatment. The following chapter will discuss specific strategies and practices that may be used with various clients with varying substance abuse and/or addiction issues.

Discussion Questions

1. What are the benefits of evaluating a client's stage of change within counseling treatment? What special considerations might you have when counseling a client who is in the precontemplation stage compared to the preparation stage? What stage of change might you categorize Dave in from the description above?
2. Based on the information related to Substance-Related Disorders from Chapter 2, would Dave meet criteria for Substance-Related Disorder?
3. What level of severity would you categorize Dave in for each dimension used by the American Society of Addiction Medicine? What level of care would you identify as most appropriate for Dave? Please provide rationale to support your assessment.

References

American Psychiatric Association. (2013). *Diagnostic and statistical manual of mental disorders* (5th ed.). Arlington, VA: American Psychiatric Association.

Belenko, S., Knight, D., Wasserman, G. A., Dennis, M. L., Wiley, T., Taxman, F. S., . . . Sales, J. (2017). The Juvenile Justice Behavioral Health Services Cascade: A new framework for measuring unmet substance use treatment services needs among adolescent offenders. *Journal of Substance Abuse Treatment, 74,* 80–91.

Brooks, F., & McHenry, B. (2015). *A contemporary approach to substance use disorders and addiction counseling* (2nd ed.). Alexandria, VA: American Counseling Association.

Butler, M., Kane, R. L., McAlpine, D., Kathol, R. G., Fu, S. S., Hagedorn, H., & Wilt, T. J. (2008). Integration of mental health/substance abuse and primary care. *Evidence Report/Technology Assessment,* (173), 1–362.

Center for Behavioral Wellness. (2016). Center for behavioral wellness. Retrieved from http://centerforbahavioralwellness.com/

Drymalski, W. M., & Nunley, M. R. (2017). Sensitivity of the ASAM criteria to psychiatric need. *International Journal of Mental Health and Addiction, 16*(3), 1–13.

Goodman, A. (1990). Addiction: Definition and implications. *Addiction, 85*(11), 1403–1408.

Jordan, C. J., & Andersen, S. L. (2017). Sensitive periods of substance abuse: Early risk for the transition to dependence. *Developmental Cognitive Neuroscience, 25,* 29–44.

Lewis, M. (2012). *Memoirs of an addicted brain: A neuroscientist examines his former life on drugs.* New York, NY: PublicAffairs.

Maclean, J. C., & Saloner, B. (2017). Substance use treatment provider behavior and healthcare reform: Evidence from Massachusetts. *Health economics, 27*(1).

Mays, V. M., Jones, A. L., Delany-Brumsey, A., Coles, C., & Cochran, S. D. (2017). Perceived discrimination in health care and mental health/substance abuse treatment among Blacks, Latinos, and Whites. *Medical Care, 55*(2), 173–181.

Mee-Lee, D. (2013). *The ASAM criteria: Treatment criteria for addictive, substance-related, and co-occurring conditions* (3rd ed.). Retrieved from https://www.asam.org/resources/the-asam-criteria/about and https://www.asam.org/resources/the-asam-criteria/text

Prochaska, J. O., & DiClemente, C. C. (1986). Toward a comprehensive model of change. In *Treating addictive behaviors* (pp. 3–27). New York, NY: Plenum.

Prochaska, J. O., DiClemente, C. C., & Norcross, J. C. (1992). In search of how people change: Applications to addictive behaviors. *American Psychologist, 47*(9), 1102.

Ringwalt, C. L., Paschall, M. J., Gitelman, A. M. (2011). Alcohol prevention strategies on college campuses and student alcohol abuse and related problems. *Journal of Drug Education, 41*(1), 99–118. doi: 10.2190/DE.41.1.f

Rutten, R. J., Broekman, T., van den Brink, W., & Schippers, G. M. (2017). Differentiating treatment-seeking substance-use disordered patients: Support for a staging model. *SUCHT.*

Saunders, J. B. (2017). Substance use and addictive disorders in DSM-5 and ICD 10 and the draft ICD 11. *Current Opinion in Psychiatry, 30*(4), 227–237.

Welsh, J. W., Knight, J. R., Hou, S. S. Y., Malowney, M., Schram, P., Sherritt, L., & Boyd, J. W. (2017). Association between substance use diagnoses and psychiatric disorders in an adolescent and young adult clinic-based population. *Journal of Adolescent Health, 60*(6), 648–652.

World Health Organization. (1992). *The ICD-10 classification of mental and behavioural disorders: Clinical descriptions and diagnostic guidelines.* Geneva: Author.

Chapter 8

Effective Counseling Strategies and Evidence-Based Practices

Matthew E. Sprong

Noel Ysasi

Lucy Parker

Megan Malone

Key Terms: evidence-based practice, motivational interviewing, cognitive behavioral therapy, dialectical behavioral therapy

Key Objectives: Students will be able to evaluate for effective counseling strategies and understand evidence-based practices among counseling professionals providing substance-related cousneling.

Treatment is the therapeutic process in which clients are exposed to emotional support and are provided education on addiction within individual, group, and/or family modalities (Brooks & McHenry, 2015). The purpose of counseling is to assist the client with exploration into barriers that prevent the client from achieving his or her treatment goals, and to process information relevant to the counseling session. There are several counseling theories that have been developed to assist a counseling professional in contributing to therapeutic change with the client. Depending on the counseling theory used, there may be a significant focus on past events (e.g., Psychoanalysis), future events (e.g., Solution-Focused Brief Therapy), or in the present moment (e.g., Acceptance and Commitment Therapy [ACT]). Despite the perception of theory purists (strong belief that their theoretical orientation is the most beneficial to develop change within the client), some scholars would suggest that a focus on all three areas (future, past, present) may be beneficial to client change and creating an eclectic approach to counseling may lead to the accomplishment of treatment goals (Corey, 2016).

Treatment provided to clients with substance-related disorders must be evidence based, meaning that research has demonstrated that it is effective in assisting clients to reach their counseling goals. To establish a treatment protocol as evidence based, there needs to be strong clinical and empirical research evidence that demonstrates the treatment modality has been effective. Empirically supported treatments are based on direct scientific evidence (e.g., several large-scale clinical trials involving thousands of clients), where the treatment modality is carefully evaluating in comparison with other treatment modalities that have been used in the past (Corey, 2016). Establishing scientific evidence involves more than relying on the counseling professionals' subjective experiencing (e.g., this treatment modality has worked with several

Contributed by Noel Ysasi; Lucy Parker; Megan Malone. © Kendall Hunt Publishing Company.

of my clients). Scientific evidence will involve years of research likely conducted in laboratory settings. Laboratory settings allow for several variables that might influence the results of the study to be controlled. For example, if a new counseling theory was being developed, researchers would have difficulty evaluating how successful the theory was if it was being used in a real-counseling setting by multiple counseling professionals. Each counseling professional may administer techniques associated with the counseling theory slightly differently or use it with other theories. Researchers may have difficulty controlling for these differences, thus reducing the conclusion and external validity of the findings. Additionally, due to privacy acts and ethical codes, researchers may be unable to record counseling sessions within real settings. Within laboratory settings, it is easier to control for these issues. However, in some instances, applied research may be used if clients are willing to agree to be evaluated for these purposes. The purpose of this chapter is to highlight evidence-based treatment approaches to counseling clients with substance-related disorders.

Evidence-Based Treatment Modalities

Oftentimes, when treating a new client in a substance use treatment facility, a client will present a lack of awareness related to how their drug and/or alcohol barriers are impacting areas of their lives (e.g., work, family). If a client is seeking treatment through a drug-court system, clients may present a lack of motivation to take their treatment process seriously. A lack of motivation of the client can result in an unsuccessful closure and prevent treatment goals from being completed.

> **Scenario 1:** Michael is a 47-year-old male from a small rural town in Haddonfield, Illinois. He currently works as a Butcher at Warren County Grove Meat Locker and is passionate about becoming a private investigator: "I am a very observant individual and usually people do not notice me when I am around." He currently lives with his sister(s) Judith and Laurie, as his wife of 20 years left with his children (named Chuck, Jason, and Freddy). Her reason for leaving is because Michael is always intoxicated after drinking several glasses of Jim Bean every night before going to bed. One night after work, Michael was arrested for driving under the influence of alcohol and was taken to the local jail overnight. Michael's sisters informed him that if he does not go to counseling treatment, he will not be able to live with them. Michael decided to seek treatment because he is afraid that if he is kicked out, he will not be able to afford an apartment and living expenses due to the child support he pays and other expenses. Michael's first meeting with his counselor was difficult. He told his counselor that he doesn't need to be in treatment and that he is only there because he needs to stay living with his sisters. He tells his counselor, "I know I drink after work and before going to bed, but I don't have a problem. . . I still go to work, I make sure the bills are paid, and I never miss any activities that my kids are involved in." Michael stated that the reason he drinks is because he has issues with a work-related situation a few years ago. Specifically, he stated "my boss Sam slipped and fell on a knife at the meat locker several years ago and he bled to death." Furthermore, Michael stated: "He was my best friend and I wasn't there to call an ambulance because I was intoxicated and Sam was covering my shift so I wouldn't get fired." He later told his counselor that he has a few times called Sam because he was too drunk to go to work and couldn't lose his job. Additionally, several years ago, he crashed the family van because he was intoxicated and Sam came and picked him up so he wouldn't be arrested. The next day, Michael called the police and told the officers that he swerved to miss hitting a deer and that his friend picked him up.

Although Michael's situation is unique in nature, it is not uncommon to have a client who is in the precontemplation stage related to their substance use. The precontemplation stage is essentially when a client is unaware that his or her behavior is problematic or produced negative consequences

(Prochaska & DiClemente, 1986; Prochaska, DiClemente, & Norcross, 1992). It is apparent that Michael does not recognize that his drinking is (a) causing him to miss work and rely on his friend to cover for him, (b) his wife left him because he was intoxicated every night before going to bed, (c) he wrecked his family's van because he was driving while intoxicated, and (d) his wife has left him due to his drinking behavior. Furthermore, he said that his friend fell and slipped on a knife at work when he was covering his shift. Despite all of these current issues, Michael still believes that his drinking is not the problem. Rather than confront Michael and tell him that these problems are related to his drinking, there are other approaches that might be more beneficial. Oftentimes, clients may become defensive when confronted, especially in the early stages of treatment for many reasons, including but not limited to (a) they do not want to be in treatment, (b) the client and counselor do not yet have a strong rapport. Prior to discussing treatment goals and developing a treatment plan or using theoretical models to assist the client in obtaining treatment goals, the counselor will need to help Michael understand how his drinking is problematic. One approach that research has found as an effective method of assisting counseling professionals with clients that are resistant to change is motivational interviewing (MI). When a client is in the precontemplation stage, it is essential to assist them in getting to the action stage (see Chapter 7 to review stages of change).

Motivational Interviewing

MI is a psychotherapeutic approach that assists a client in moving away from a state of indecision or uncertainty toward finding motivation to make positive decisions and accomplishing established goals. Developed in the late 1980s by Dr. William Miller and Dr. Stephen Rollnick (Miller & Moyers, 2017), MI is a treatment intervention that is a collaborative, person-centered form of guiding to elicit and strengthen motivation for change (Miller & Rollnick, 2002).

MI was established on five principles (Center for Substance Abuse Treatment, 1999), including (1) express empathy through reflective listening, (2) develop discrepancy between clients' goals or values and their current behavior, (3) avoid argument and direct confrontation [roll with resistance], (4) adjust to client resistance rather than opposing it directly, and (5) support self-efficacy and optimism. When a client is ambivalent about change, the use of MI can assist in reducing this ambivalence and helping the client take action. Sobell and Sobell (2011) described several techniques used in MI (see Table 1). A skilled counseling professional will evaluate the client's readiness for change and utilize the techniques listed and described below.

Open-ended questions are beneficial to use in counseling because it allows a client to share their stories with the counseling professional. Closed-ended questions are those that can be answered with a simple yes or no (e.g., Michael, do you miss your family?), whereas open-ended questions require more thought (e.g., Michael, what has it been like since you haven't lived with your family?). Open-ended questions also allow clients to describe events from their standpoint (allows for assessment into their thinking) and engage in further self-analysis. Sometimes, clients do not process events or information and the counselor can assist in this by asking them open-ended questions versus closed-ended questions. Open-ended questions

Table 1 Techniques of Motivational Interviewing

Open-ended questions	Feedback
Positive Affirmations	Asking Permission
Reflections/Reflective Listening	Normalizing
Summaries	Readiness to Change Ruler/Scaling
Change-Talk	Columbo Approach

will allow the client to explore reasons for and possibility of change. Some examples of questions that Michael's counseling professional could ask include:

- What happens when your children see you intoxicated?
- What would happen if your children saw you intoxicated?
- What is the worst thing that would happen if you continue drinking?
- What would it take for you to think about making a change?

Positive *Affirmations* are used in MI to assist in changing a client's belief about certain aspects of their own lives by removing old negative beliefs that were creating difficulty with positive change. The counseling professional will recognize a client's strengths, successes, and efforts to change throughout the counseling process. This helps in increasing the client's confidence in their ability to change. For example, if a client was discussing how they are not progressing in their treatment recovery, a counseling professional could affirm positive changes already made in their lives (e.g., you continue to come back to counseling so you must be taking this seriously, you have completed these short-term goals and haven't used marijuana in 4 weeks).

Reflections/Reflective Listening is a technique that is used to show a client that the counseling professional is present in the moment and is engaged in the counseling process. The counseling professional is seeking to understand the client by paraphrasing (summarizing) what the client just stated. These *summary statements* are used to show the client that you are actively listening to what they are stating while also initiating an opportunity for the client to reflect on what they have just stated:

Michael (*client*): My wife has left me with my kids, I am now living with my sisters because I can't afford to live on my own. I was just arrested for driving under the influence of alcohol, and I am not sure how I am going to get out of this mess.

Counselor: It appears you have several challenges that you are currently facing that are adding additional stress in your life and you are not sure how to manage these barriers?

There are several components to the reflective statement that should be noted. The counseling professional demonstrates that they are actively listening to the client while also providing an opportunity for the client to continue to discuss these issues. If the counseling professional correctly interpreted the client, they will likely acknowledge this and continue to share their story. Another benefit of making this reflective statement is that it provides the client an opportunity to correct the counseling professional if they are not interpreting it correctly. Below are three examples of counselor responses that are inappropriate or could become problematic:

Counselor (statement 1): If you would quit drinking you likely wouldn't have these problems that you are discussing now.

Counselor (statement 2): Let's talk about something important like your current employment status.

Counselor (statement 3): What are the specific legal issues you are facing?

In the first example, the counseling professional is attributing all of the problems to the drinking behavior and this might create an inferior–superior relationship between the client and counseling professional. This response may also appear confrontational to the client and they may become defensive toward the counseling professional. The second statement made by the counseling professional is inappropriate as it will make the client (a) become defensive, or (b) feel like what they are saying is not important. Both of these issues may become problematic in attempting to move toward positive change. In the third example, the client is leading the session rather than providing the client an opportunity to speak about what is on their mind. The statement made by the client is likely an emotional one, and it is important for the counseling professional to explore these feelings and this statement. By picking one point made by the client, the counseling professional is not allowing the client to reflect on the statement just made by them.

Change-talk is a technique that counseling professionals use to evaluate change in how the client interprets their unwanted behavior. For example, oftentimes clients may have a desire to change (I wish I could quit smoking) but the method in which they phrase the desire shows they do not have much confidence in their ability to change. The change-talk technique can be described by the D-A-R-N acronym. **D** stands for <u>desire</u> to change and the client will use words such as I wish I could, I want to do this, I would like to. The **A** stands for <u>ability</u> and is conceptualized as the client starts to gain confidence that they could make a change. The client may use words such as I could quit, I can stop. The **R** stands for <u>reasons</u> and is related to the client justifying what could happen if they made a change. The client may make statements such as If I find new friends that do not use drugs, I could maintain my sobriety. The **N** stands for <u>need</u> and is related to the necessity to change. Clients may make statements such as I can't keep up this lifestyle. The counseling professional should also pay attention to commitment language such as I am prepared to quit using drugs, or I intend to change. Language is oftentimes a powerful indicator of how committed a client is to change. For example, a client who makes the statement "I may change" versus a client who makes the statement "I will change" likely have different motivation levels or commitment to change levels.

Feedback is a technique that counselors use to help clients make decisions with added knowledge (Sobell & Sobell, 2011). It is important to not confuse feedback with lecturing or judging as in MI lecturing or judging is not helpful. Specifically, for a counselor to give feedback, they may invite and ask their client "would you like to learn more about. . . .?" Another phrase that could be used includes: "Let's take a minute to talk about . . ." Next, a client may ask a question about why knowledge on their topic matters. A counselor could use national data to talk about reasons that relate to their topic. For example, when considering addiction, clients may be ready to change, but may have less knowledge about the effects of their addiction. A counselor may talk with the client about the prevalence of addiction and the side effects that occur due to their substance of choice. An exact example would be: "You talk about wanting to change your habit of smoking. This is a hard habit to change as 20%-40% of people are able to quit within their first year (US News, 2018). With smoking being a difficult substance to quit, how can we talk about preparing for imperfection and potential relapse, if relapse does unfortunately occur?" In the prior example, as in other examples of feedback, a counselor uses information to help the client become further aware of their change (Sobell & Sobell, 2011). Feedback could be used in a question as in this previous sentence or feedback could also occur in brief information bits throughout a session. Learning about a person's presenting concern may help them to better understand how to change as well as give them extra cognitive motivation to change. Other ways that counselors provide feedback in addition to verbal feedback throughout collaborative, egalitarian style sessions include giving clients handouts to review between sessions.

Asking Permission is a technique that counselors use to invite their client to further explore or discuss a salient topic in session (Sobell & Sobell, 2011). For example, a client may have referenced an addictive behavior in a previous session and a counselor may link this topic by the technique of asking permission. Specifically, for a client who has previously mentioned a desire to quit smoking in a previous session may be asked by a counselor "can I hear a little more about your goal to quit smoking?" Other ways to ask permission include "can we talk a bit more about . . . ?" or "can we go back to . . . that you mentioned earlier?" Asking permission is intended to continue to show the client care, compassion, and empathy which will add rapport, Socratic questioning, and information gathering. Asking permission aligns with robust research theorists who have found that when invited or asked permission, clients are more likely to talk in therapy versus when told to do so in a less empathetic way.

Normalizing is a technique that counselors use to help clients validate themselves and feel humanized or related with others when talking about their presenting concerns (Sobell & Sobell, 2011). An example of normalizing a client while helping them with other MI techniques includes "a lot of people have smoked to cope with stress before . . ."This phrase relates a client's past behavior to those of others. Normalization also helps clients decrease their own reservations or self-shame related to talking with their counselor. A counselor may normalize a client's intentions, mistakes, or behaviors, and then help a client to become aware of their desired change. Moreover, a counselor may normalize any shame a client shows regarding initially engaging in an addiction and then in a following session(s), help the client (with the rapport gained through normalization) become aware of their discrepancies (which is another MI technique). Normalization is also considered a way that counselors can help clients feel less alone in their presenting issue. Similar to other techniques in MI, normalization is focused on helping a client to foster their own change, while not being obstructed by self-shame or feelings of relatedness (Sobell & Sobell, 2011).

Readiness to Change/Scaling is the process of using a scale (that is directional) to assess how willing a client is to change an unwanted behavior. For example, a counseling professional could ask the client to rate on a scale of 1 to 10 (1 = not at all ready to change and 10 is completely ready to change), where is the client in the process of changing their drug use behavior. Oftentimes, a client in the precontemplation stage will provide a rating closer to 1. A client's readiness to change can change from day-to-day, and this scale can lead to further discussion. Consider the following example(s) in the script below:

> *Counseling Professional:* Allison, I want you to take a look at the following scale. As you will see, the scale ranges from 1 to 10, with 1 indicating not ready at all and 10 indicating that you are completely ready to change. Do you understand the scale I am giving you?
> *Client:* Yes.
> *Counseling Professional:* Using the following scale, how likely are you to change your drug use behavior?
> *Client:* Four.

The counseling professional has a few different directions in terms of using the readiness to change ruler within the counseling session. For example, the counseling professional can ask the client to explain why they gave the numerical value of 4 rather than 3 (What's the difference between these two numbers). The counseling professional can also ask what the difference between the rating of 4 and 6. Once the client explains the difference, the counseling professional can ask what obstacles prevent the client from getting to the rating of 6. This process allows the client to begin an exploration phase. The counseling professional should be cautious when asking questions. If a client were to provide the rating of a 2, and the counseling professional asked what it would take to get to a 10, the client might feel overwhelmed and this goal might seem unattainable, thus leading to the client giving up prior to engaging in the treatment process. The readiness to change scaling technique is beneficial because it allows a counseling professional to assess the progress that a client has experienced from treatment. The counseling professional could also ask the client to provide a rating on a scale related to how confident they will be able to make a change, or to complete an action step in the treatment plan (see Chapter 10) to assess any barriers that need to be addressed.

The *Columbo approach* involves addressing discrepancies in a nonconfrontational manner in an attempt to assist the client in reflecting on these discrepancies. As aforementioned, oftentimes when a client is confronted about a behavior, the client will become defensive. When a client is defensive it is difficult to make progress in treatment. However, as the client is making statements, a well-trained counseling professional will identify discrepancies. The Columbo approach is a method to confront the discrepancy in a nonadversarial manner. For example, a counseling professional might state the following:

> *Client:* I use to enjoy going out with my friends several years ago. We were all single and after work on Friday we would all go to Fast Eddies for burgers and beer. They are all married now and I am drinking there by myself. I recently loss my job and was arrested for driving under the influence. I wonder if I could meet new people to go out to the bar with, or perhaps find friends that want to do other things.

Counseling Professional: You stated that when you first started drinking several years ago you enjoyed your time spent with your friends and it was a break from reality. Now it sounds like you have increased your drinking and with your recent loss of employment and most recent arrest, you are considering drinking.

Scenario 2: Roberta, 53, an attractive woman, dressed in high heels and a form-fitting dress, and wearing tasteful makeup comes into your office. From a first impression, Roberta looks like anything but someone addicted to substances. Roberta shares with you that she is from Southern Brazil, but that she moved to the United States after earning her Master's degree in Business Administration (MBA). Roberta reported that she is separated from her husband. She shared that she also has one young adult daughter but is currently living alone as her daughter has begun her first year of college. Roberta shares that she is seeking treatment for "issues I'm having because of my drinking." She shared with you that she will lose her 12-year American position in her business if she doesn't stop drinking. She elaborates that she feels estranged from her family and her friends because of her drinking. Roberta shared with you that she has tried Alcoholics Anonymous (AA), but is having great difficulty finding a sponsor ("I am one of the only women, little lone women of color in the groups I have attended"). Roberta also shared that she is also having trouble relating to other women in the program ("They're not very talkative. Maybe because I'm Latina and have a strong accent."). When asked about her personal relationships with others outside of AA, she looks down and mumbles something noncommittal. When you (as the counseling professional) ask, "have you been in any long-term relationship with anyone, friends or spouse, in the past 12 years?" Roberta shares that she was close to her daughter and shared that "I loved our fun times together, but I am glad she is bettering herself now in school." You, then ask Roberta if she can say more about the nature of she and her daughter's relationship, the quality of it, and the reasons for her mentioning this relationship and not others. Roberta answers in ambivalent terms that she and her daughter "bickered about how much I drank" and that her daughter felt "she had to leave my lifestyle." When reflecting Roberta's content shared, Roberta begins to cry and she shares "I have needed this for a long time." You, her counselor, must now decide whether to ask for more information and what to do with that information to help Roberta. As a reminder, your questions and facilitation are intended to assess Roberta's substance use and are driven to facilitate the most appropriate treatment for Roberta. What will you do? Where will you begin? What level of care, approaches, and treatment seem most congruent for Roberta? After addressing your appropriate care, think about how common myths and stereotypes may be relevant to this case. To counteract varying stigmas, stereotypes, and myths about addiction, what are Roberta's strengths and resiliencies? Now that you have considered your own evaluation, the section below will address various modality examples to help Roberta.

One example of MI includes the counseling professional asking a client to consider what is the "worst thing" that could or may happen if they continue with their current addiction (Miller & Moyers, 2017). Comparatively, a counseling professional would then also ask about the "best thing" that a client may experience as a potential result of abstinence or decreased usage.

When considering Roberta, a counseling professional may ask Roberta various Socratic questions (Miller & Moyers, 2017; Miller & Rollnick, 2002). These questions may include: "what do you believe is the worst thing that will happen if you continue your drinking?" and "You mention wanting to be clues with your daughter, but you drink which seems to drive your daughter away; do you notice this discrepancy?" As you continue to work with Roberta using MI, you may also educate her regarding the consequences of addiction, which also facilitates her own awareness about the impact of drinking. You may also expect that

Roberta may provide minimal defensiveness during this process. It is important for you, as the helper, to continuously empathize with Roberta while also at times, re-presenting her discrepancies. Your continued empathy includes MI in particularly your rolling with any potential resistance or defensiveness Roberta may have in regard to processing about and in changing her drinking.

Cognitive Behavioral Therapy

Cognitive behavioral therapy (CBT) in one of the most established and empirically validated therapies in substance abuse counseling (Dobson & Dobson, 2016; Hassan, Bhatia, & Bhatia, 2017; Smout et al., 2010). CBT emphasizes that a client's thoughts causes feelings and behaviors, with a goal of working toward acceptance of one's self, of others, and of life. CBT also recognizes various physiological processes that may influence a client's abusive or addictive behaviors. One example of a client's physiological catalysts to abuse and/or addiction may be brain chemistry. The brain chemistry of clients may be impacted as clients may use or abuse substances to mimic various pleasure centers in their brain. In addition to potential brain chemistry and genetic relations, clients with substance abuse or addiction issues may present with high-risk situations, cognitive risk factors, negative thoughts, and self-esteem issues. To address various issues that may be interrelated to the client's abuse and/or addiction, counseling professionals using the CBT theory use a combination of strategies to teach clients about their 1) thoughts, 2) emotions, and 3) behaviors, and the interrelatedness of these concepts. Clients are specifically given psychoeducation about potential cognitive distortions (i.e., which are faulty thinking patterns) that may reinforce their abuse and/or addiction. Other thinking patterns including denial, rationalization, minimization, blaming, intellectualization, justification, and explanation may also be explored with a client and a CBT-oriented helper to find "the core belief" which may be influencing their abuse and/or addiction. The figure below represents a cognitive model of negative thinking (Corey, 2016).

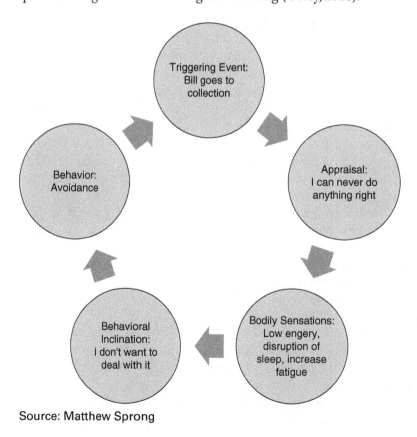

Source: Matthew Sprong

CBT opines that if a client is unable to control their oppressive thoughts and emotions, they will be ruled by them (e.g., I am killing myself with my fears, I must stop feeling anxious right now, I can't recover). Negative thoughts that a client may have include (1) problem magnification, (2) overgeneralization, (3) urgency (e.g., I must stop feeling anxious now), (4) helplessness and resignation (e.g., I can't do anything to fix my situation), and (5) circular thinking.

Rational emotive behavioral therapy (REBT) is a form of CBT in which a client is encouraged to examine and change irrational thought patterns (irrational thinking) and beliefs in order to reduce dysfunctional behavior (Corey, 2016). Moreover, a number of core beliefs underlie most unhelpful emotions and behaviors, and CORE beliefs are underlying rules that guide how people react to the events and circumstances in their lives. For example, a client might have the following self-defeating irrational beliefs:

1. I need love and approval from those around me.
2. Events in my past are the cause of my problems—and they continue to influence my feelings and behaviors now.
3. I should become upset when other people have problems and feel unhappy when they're sad.

REBT opines that our CORE beliefs (e.g., Helpless, Unlovable, Worthless) produce automatic thoughts when situations arise. When a stressful situation arises, we develop automatic thoughts that lead to (1) a physiological response, (2) emotional response, and (3) behavioral response. Grohol (2018) provided several examples of cognitive distortions to assist a counseling professional in identifying irrational thoughts, including:

1. Filtering: focusing solely on the negative and ignoring all the positive.
2. Polarized thinking: Black and white thinking, not seeing the gray area.
3. Overgeneralization: Assuming all experiences and people are the same, based on one negative experience.
4. Jumping to conclusions: Being convinced of something with little to no evidence to support it.
5. Catastrophizing: Assuming the worst-case scenario, magnifying the negative and minimizing the positive.
6. Personalization: Believing that you are at least partially responsible for everything bad that happens around you.
7. Control fallacies: Thinking everything that happens to you is either all your fault or not at all your fault.
8. Fallacy of fairness: Being too concerned over whether everything is fair.
9. Blaming: Pointing to others when looking for a cause of any negative event, instead of looking at yourself.
10. Shoulds: Holding tight to your personal rules on how people ought to behave.
11. Emotional reasoning: Believing if I feel it, it must be true.
12. Fallacy of change: Expecting others to change to suit your needs or desires.

There are many other cognitive distortions that are discussed in other counseling theory textbooks. However, these are some examples of how clients might view situations or the world that surround them. Consider the following example:

Scenario 3: Johnna was enrolled in master's level behavioral analysis courses with the goal of becoming a board-certified behavioral analyst (BCBA). Approximately 3 months after taking the BCBA examination, Johnna received a letter indicating that she did not pass the exam. Johnna's initial thought was that she was worthless and not smart enough to become a BCBA (automatic thought). After Johnna read the exam results, her heart began to race (physiological response), she experienced feelings of sadness, worry, and anger (emotional response), and decided to take several prescription medications at the same time (behavioral response).

What cognitive distortions is Johnna making? Is there another thought pattern that might assist Johnna in looking at the scenario in a healthier manner?

There are several techniques to assist a client who has negative or irrational thoughts like Johnna that might be beneficial to use when working with clients who have problems manifesting from drugs and/ or alcohol. The first technique is the ABC model. The A stands for **Activating Event**, the B stands for **Beliefs (thoughts, attitudes, assumptions)** about the event, and the C stands for **Consequences** (feelings, emotions, behaviors, actions) stemming from the beliefs about the events. The goal of the ABC technique is to identify the irrational beliefs in situations described by the client and assist them in disputing the beliefs so that the consequences change. This can be accomplished by exploring a client's thoughts, affect, and behaviors when describing an event that occurred. For example, if a client was discussing an argument that took place with their significant other, a counseling professional could explore their thoughts before, during, and after the argument, what led to the argument, what were they feeling before, during, or after the argument. Once the client has processed an event comprehensively, the counseling professional can employ the ABC technique. Consider the following example related to Johnna:

Activating Event: Johnna failed her BCBA examination
Irrational Belief: She feels worthless and unintelligent
Consequence: Johnna drops out of the master's degree program

The goal would be to have Johnna work on finding an alternative to view her situation from a more positive perspective. Disputing irrational beliefs involves three steps, including detecting (identifying the "should" and "must"), debating (client argues themselves out of believing and acting on irrational beliefs), and discriminating (client learns to discriminate irrational [self-defeating] beliefs from rational [self-helping] beliefs). Once a client becomes skilled at disputing irrational beliefs, they will form a new effective philosophy (new belief system).

Another technique that is commonly used in CBT is *systematic desensitization*, which is a method to remove the fear response of a phobia (Corey 2016). When a person has fear related to some anxiety-provoking situation, there are two methods that can be used in an attempt to assist the person in overcoming their fear. The first is called flooding, in which the client would be placed in the anxiety-provoking event immediately. For example, if a person was scared of heights, if we used the *flooding technique* we could have them jump out of an airplane, stand on a roof, or walk near a ledge of a cliff. The other technique (systematic desensitization) is a method in which the client would gradually work toward eliminating their fear by taking several smaller anxiety-provoking steps. For example, the person who is afraid of heights might start off by standing on a step stool, then proceeding to stand on a short ladder, then a taller ladder, then perhaps standing on the roof. As in this example, the person is taking incremental steps that would increase anxiety to a less intense degree than having them jump out of an airplane. Whether one technique is greater than the other will be up to the counseling professional as they will have to use their clinical judgment and make goals collaboratively with the client. *Homework activities* are oftentimes used as a method to have the client process events, situations, or anything related to the accomplishment of treatment goals between their counseling sessions. For example, in scenario 1, Michael had several issues that arose from his alcohol use. A counseling professional using CBT might have Michael make a list of the pros and cons of his drinking behavior. This activity would require Michael to spend some considerable time making the list but might also assist him in recognizing that the negatives outweigh the positives and perhaps change is needed. If Michael is unable to develop a list of negatives, this can be accomplished during a counseling session with further exploration between the counseling professional and the client. Other examples of CBT and Rational Emotive Behavioral techniques include cognitive homework, bibliotherapy, psychoeducational methods, rational emotive imagery, and shame-attacking exercises.

Let's explore a CBT oriented example with Roberta . . .

When considering Roberta, a counseling professional guided by CBT may provide Roberta with psychoeducation about the triad of thoughts, feelings, and behaviors. Roberta would be asked about her automatic and current core thoughts about herself, her world, and her drinking. She would then work with the therapist to track her thoughts that may trigger her drinking. For example, a counseling professional may encourage Roberta to complete a weekly thought log to investigate on which thoughts she experiences when triggered to drink. These thoughts would be processed as well as related emotions. Thought-stopping and challenging negative thoughts would then be encouraged by the helper for Roberta to help her minimize her triggers. Substitute behaviors that are alternatives to drinking will also be explored. Lastly, Roberta would be encouraged to co-facilitate and co-construct either abstinence based and/or de-scaffolded goals for her to decrease her drinking. Her goals would be written and continuously asked about in therapy.

Dialectical Behavior Therapy (DBT)

Marsha Linehan developed DBT in the late 1980s due to her work with clients who had suicidal ideation (Sharf, 2015). Later, she would develop the theory to be primarily used for clients with borderline personality disorder, but DBT has often been known to be quite successful for persons with substance use disorders (SUD), eating disorders, anxiety disorders, depression, and trauma-based issues (Corey, 2016). Within the context of behavior therapy, the term "dialectics" refers to a fundamental nature of reality and a therapeutic approach consisting of persuasive dialogue and relationship (Kegan, 1982). The philosophical orientation of dialectics emphasizes wholeness, interrelatedness, and process (change) (Corey, 2016). The overall premise of DBT is that people are not simple beings. Humans are complex in nature and are behaviorally influenced through people, work, innate characteristics, and life's challenges. For instance, if Mandy went to work and had a bad day, what conclusions are you drawn to? Maybe you thought Mandy's job stressed her out. By using DBT, we try to understand that several factors are at play, and we should not assume one specific thing is the direct cause of how a person feels (i.e., her job). Instead, we try to evaluate the entirety of the person and environment, which may contribute to the thoughts that one feels. For example, what if Mandy received a call during work that her father was recently in a car accident? Unfortunately, most novice counselors immediately go with their gut reaction rather than fully assessing the entirety of a client's presenting problem. As a result, the treatment outcome is generally unsuccessful and why this theoretical model is continuing to gain wide acceptance throughout the counseling community.

DBT stands from the position of guiding the clinician in developing a theoretical hypothesis relevant to the client's problems and to the treatment. In addition, the theory has been so effective for clients with SUD, due to its ability to provide practitioners with clear direction on the use of DBT. For example, when providing counseling services to individuals with a substance use disorder (SUD), the importance lies with (a) recognizing catalyst to the development of SUD and (b) what treatment approach would best serve my client? However, some key guiding features of dialectics influence the therapeutic approach, which consist of the following: (1) defining the disorder; (2) identifying how the effects of the disorder are long-term in nature whereby they directly affect one's health; and (3) recognizing how the disorder is often the result of multiple factors and not just one (Hollandsworth, 1990).

However, its application to specific disorders is often applied for therapists seeking to assist their clients in regulating emotions and behavior (Corey, 2016). DBT integrates cognitive behavioral concepts in conjunction with mindfulness training (generally known as Zen practice) (Linehan, 1993). Moreover, DBT teaches clients both mindfulness and acceptance. The concept of acceptance requires the client to learn how to "accept" life as it is, seeing reality without distortions, without judgment, evaluations, and hanging on to an experience for a prolonged period of time (Corey, 2016; Robins, Schmidt, & Linehan, 2004). Mindfulness skills, however, require the client to focus on breathing, staying within the present (i.e., focusing on one activity), identifying and describing feelings, attending to emotions, letting thoughts flow, being nonjudgmental, and accepting of one's feelings (Corey, 2016).

Scenario. John is a professor at an Ivy League institution and has two children. He has four children and a beautiful wife. John has always considered himself blessed with a wonderful family and great colleagues. One day, John finds out his wife has cheated on him. Soon after, he finds himself not showing up to work, is often intoxicated, and starting using methamphetamines. Soon after he has started to show signs at the office of his unprofessional behavior, John was called into the Dean's office and was given a choice to either resign or clean up his act. John quickly becomes nervous and agrees to improve on his overall behavior. However, shortly after the meeting, he decides to go out for one last drink and takes some pills to numb the pain, but most importantly, he makes a promise to himself that this will be the last time. After leaving the local bar inebriated, John is pulled over by the cops and taken into custody. Luckily for John, he did not have to show up to work until he lectured the following week. However, he was court mandated to attend group counseling and receive 20 hours of individualized counseling treatment.

Questions:

1. Based on John's scenario, what first steps would you take toward addressing his SUD?
2. What would your next step be? What methods would you use to ensure John is focusing on the DBT counseling principles?
3. What methods would you use to make sure John is following through with the agreed upon goals of counseling set by you and him?

Case of Roberta

When using DBT to help Roberta, a counselor would talk with Roberta about her current ways of coping. Harm reduction to improve distress tolerance would be one of the main aspects and initial aspects of session. Another salient intervention for Roberta would be to explore her current emotional distress when not using her substance (drinking). Roberta would be asked to log her negative emotions and would also be asked of other ways that she may experience these emotions without using alcohol. Additionally, identifying emotional processes and potential family or origin, trauma, and/or other environmental stressors that may needed to be explored to help Roberta improve her emotional regulation and increase her distress tolerance will also be processed. DBT worksheets to help ground Roberta in the various aspects of DBT may also be utilized and to continue to keep structure within the trajectory of DBT-related counseling sessions.

Acceptance and Commitment Therapy

ACT, similar to DBT, is a relatively new therapy approach. Developed in part by Dr. Steven Hayes, ACT focuses on clients gaining self-awareness and psychological flexibility (Hayes, Strosahl, & Wilson, 2012). ACT therapists assert that when clients are rigid psychologically they may also be separated from their values and life purposes (Chiesa & Serretti, 2014). Helping clients gain acceptance of the present moment, gaining mindfulness, gaining emotional and psychological flexibility, and accepting oneself with their problems (while not defining themselves from these problems) are ways that ACT therapists facilitate client change (Chiesa & Serretti, 2014; Hayes et al., 2012). More specifically, ACT-guided helpers may influence client psychological flexibility and change by deconstructing rigid psychological rules that clients present such as, "would haves, could haves, and should haves." Clients are encouraged to embrace the present moment even with negative feelings or discomfort and accept these fallibilities along with their imperfect selves (Chiesa & Serretti, 2014; Hayes et al., 2012).

ACT is a behavioral based therapy that focuses on accepting the behaviors which occur throughout the natural environment instead of replacing them with different behaviors, as seen in cognitive behavior therapy (CBT). ACT focuses around utilizing metaphors to aid the client within their treatment. To provide a little background, ACT is a functional contextual therapy approach based on Relational Frame Theory that views human psychological problems dominantly as problems of psychological inflexibility fostered by cognitive fusion and experiential avoidance. In the context of a therapeutic relationship, ACT brings direct contingencies and indirect verbal processes to bear on the experiential establishment of greater psychological flexibility primarily through acceptance, defusion, establishment of a transcendent sense of self, contact with the present moment, values, and building larger and larger patterns of committed action linked to those values. Said more simply, ACT uses acceptance and mindfulness processes, and commitment and behavior change processes, to produce greater psychological flexibility.

ACT aims to decrease avoidance of these inner experiences as the dominant response to anxiety. The repertoire of responses in anxiety is broadened, thus resulting in *psychological flexibility* (defined as the ability to openly experience anxiety while moving in personally chosen directions). This is accomplished through targeting the six psychological processes thought to be responsible for the onset and maintenance of anxiety disorders from an ACT perspective: being present, acceptance, defusion, self as context, values, and committed action (Hayes et al., 2006). The six psychological processes are colloquially coined as the "Hexaflex." The six processes are interconnected, where the four processes on the left of the hexaflex are associated with mindfulness and acceptance processes while the four processes on the right are associated with committed and behavioral activation.

Acceptance

Acceptance is taught as an alternative to experiential avoidance. Acceptance involves the active and aware embrace of those private events occasioned by one's history without unnecessary attempts to change their frequency or form, especially when doing so would cause psychological harm. For example, anxiety patients are taught to feel anxiety, as a feeling, fully and without defense; pain patients are given methods that encourage them to let go of a struggle with pain, and so on. Acceptance (and defusion) in ACT is not an end in itself. Rather acceptance is fostered as a method of increasing values-based action.

Cognitive Fusion

Cognitive defusion techniques attempt to alter the undesirable functions of thoughts and other private events, rather than trying to alter their form, frequency, or situational sensitivity. Said another way, ACT attempts to change the way one interacts with or relates to thoughts by creating contexts in which their unhelpful functions are diminished. There are scores of such techniques that have been developed for a wide variety of clinical presentations. For example, a negative thought could be watched dispassionately, repeated out loud until only its sound remains, or treated as an externally observed event by giving it a shape, size, color, speed, or form. A person could thank their mind for such an interesting thought, label the process of thinking ("I am having the thought that I am no good"), or examine the historical thoughts, feelings, and memories that occur while they experience that thought. Such procedures attempt to reduce the literal quality of the thought, weakening the tendency to treat the thought as what it refers to ("I am no good") rather than what it is directly experienced to be (e.g., the thought "I am no good"). The result of defusion is usually a decrease in believability of, or attachment to, private events rather than an immediate change in their frequency.

Being Present

ACT promotes ongoing nonjudgmental contact with psychological and environmental events as they occur. The goal is to have clients experience the world more directly so that their behavior is more flexible and thus their actions more consistent with the values that they hold. This is accomplished by allowing workability to exert more control over behavior; and by using language more as a tool to note and describe events, not simply to predict and judge them. A sense of self called "self as process" is actively encouraged: the defused, nonjudgmental ongoing description of thoughts, feelings, and other private events.

Self as Context

As a result of relational frames such as I versus You, Now versus Then, and Here versus There, human language leads to a sense of self as a locus or perspective, and provides a transcendent, spiritual side to normal verbal humans. This idea was one of the seeds from which both ACT and Relational Frame Theory grew and there is now growing evidence of its importance to language functions such as empathy, theory of mind, sense of self, and the like. In brief, the idea is that "I" emerges over large sets of exemplars of perspective-taking relations (what are termed in RFT "deictic relations"), but since this sense of self is a context for verbal knowing, not the content of that knowing, its limits cannot be consciously known. Self as context is important in part because from this standpoint, one can be aware of one's own flow of experiences without attachment to them or an investment in which particular experiences occur: thus defusion and acceptance are fostered. Self as context is fostered in ACT by mindfulness exercises, metaphors, and experiential processes.

Values

Values are chosen qualities of purposive action that can never be obtained as an object but can be instantiated moment by moment. ACT uses a variety of exercises to help a client choose life directions in various domains (e.g., family, career, spirituality) while undermining verbal processes that might lead to choices based on avoidance, social compliance, or fusion (e.g., "I should value X" or "A good person would value Y" or "My mother wants me to value Z"). In ACT, acceptance, defusion, being present, and so on are not ends in themselves; rather they clear the path for a more vital, values-consistent life.

Committed Action

Finally, ACT encourages the development of larger and larger patterns of effective action linked to chosen values. In this regard, ACT looks very much like traditional behavior therapy, and almost any behaviorally coherent behavior change method can be fitted into an ACT protocol, including exposure, skills acquisition, shaping methods, goal setting, and the like. Unlike values, which are constantly instantiated but never achieved as an object, concrete goals that are values consistent can be achieved and ACT protocols almost always involve therapy work and homework linked to short-, medium-, and long-term behavior change goals. Behavior change efforts in turn lead to contact with psychological barriers that are addressed through other ACT processes (acceptance, defusion, and so on).

Taken as a whole, each of these processes supports the other and all target psychological flexibility: the process of contacting the present moment fully as a conscious human being and persisting or changing behavior in the service of chosen values. The six processes can be chunked into two groupings. Mindfulness and acceptance processes involve acceptance, defusion, contact with the present moment, and self as context. Indeed, these four processes provide a workable behavioral definition of mindfulness (see Fletcher & Hayes, in press in the publications section). Commitment and behavior change processes involve contact with the present moment, self as context, values, and committed action. Contact with the present moment and self as context occur in both groupings because all psychological activity of conscious human beings involves the now as known.

Case of Roberta

When working with Roberta, a counseling professional using ACT may first process Roberta's feelings about her drinking. Roberta may exhibit self-shame. Helping Roberta challenge her negative thoughts such as, "I should have done more as a mother to my now adult daughter," may help Roberta to accept her true self and begin to reduce and/or abstain from her alcohol usage. Another deconstruction that an ACT-guided helper may pursue with Roberta could be, "that joy and fun are associated with drinking." A counseling professional may also ask Roberta what other substitute behaviors bring her joy in the present moment. Helping Roberta to accept that she may also relapse with efforts to reduce and abstain from alcohol would be the salient goal of ACT therapy, which also focuses on Roberta's self-acceptance, mindfulness, and to gain psychological flexibility.

Substance-Related Disorders and Vocational Rehabilitation

Traditionally, vocational rehabilitation (VR) services have not been readily available to individuals undergoing substance abuse treatment (Center for Substance Abuse Treatment[CSAT], 2000). Glenn, Huber, Keferl, Wright-Bell, and Lane (2008) suggested VR services with treatment of SUDs should emphasize a holistic and individualized approach, empowering individuals to reach treatment and employment goals. Employment has shown to be a significant factor in completion of substance abuse treatment and increased quality of life (Brickham, Jeong Han, Gonzalez, & Rosenthal, 2016; Lusk, 2018; Melvin, Davis, & Koch, 2012; Petry, Andrade, Rash, & Cherniack, 2014).

Petry et al. (2014) analyzed substance use, employment, and quality of life factors in individuals who engaged in employment-related activities during a 12-week, reinforcement-based, outpatient treatment program. The results showed that individuals who engaged in at least two employment-related activities remained in treatment longer and stayed abstinent for longer periods compared to those who did not engage in employment-related activities. Individuals returning to work who have maintained sobriety often face many issues in maintaining employment, including the ability to concentrate, maintain attendance, attaining appropriate work attire, and transportation (Brickham et al., 2016). Additionally, Petry et al. (2014) found that demographic characteristics were relatively similar among individuals who were successful with engagement in employment-related activities, with the exception of age and gender which were controlled.

Pete et al. (2015) identified treatment outcomes with employment for African American males with SUDs. Traditionally, VR services shown to be successful with employment for individuals undergoing substance abuse treatment include job development, job placement, referral services, and skills training. Forty-five percent of participants gained competitive employment after completion of VR services, including job readiness training, job placement and development, educational training, transportation services, on-the-job supports, maintenance services, and rehabilitation technology. Direct job placement services showed to be a higher predictor of employment success as opposed to job-skills training and job-seeking assistance (Pete et al., 2015). These results suggest that it may be more successful to match individuals directly to open positions upon the completion of VR services, as individuals with SUDs are often faced with stigma in employment. Similarly, Lusk (2018) identified services predicting gainful employment from the Rehabilitation Services Administration (2010-2014), finding on-the-job support and job placement to be the top predictors of successful employment among individuals with SUD. The Center for Substance Abuse Treatment (2000) suggests individuals with SUDs lack adequate job histories, which provides further evidence that VR services related to job placement and training could be successful for individuals with SUD obtaining competitive employment.

Many state VR agencies require sobriety waiting periods before consumers can receive treatment for SUDs (Brickham et al., 2016). Individuals in the sobriety waiting period can wait at least 90 days before obtaining VR services (Heinemann, Moore, Lazowski, Huber, & Semik, 2014). This can be problematic for individuals who are unemployed during the waiting period because they are in a vulnerable state and may be less motivated to comply with treatment as time passes with no assistance (Brickham et al., 2016). Another conflict with VR services in the treatment of SUDs is the lack of recognition of SUD by counselors (CSAT, 2011; Glenn et al., 2008; Sprong, Dallas, Melvin, & Koch, 2014). Separation of VR services and substance abuse treatment is a common issue seen among research for employment predictors as a factor of treatment (Lusk, 2018; Sprong et al., 2014) According to SAMHSA's National Survey on Drug Use and Health, in 2014, 21.5 million Americans reported having a SUD in the past year, including those with co-occurring conditions (CBHSQ, 2015). A primary goal of VR services in addition to helping PWD obtain competitive employment is providing appropriate referral when needed to address specific needs (Sprong et al., 2014). If recognition of SUD among VR counselors and the lack of referrals is present, many individuals with SUD may not be receiving adequate services to obtain competitive employment.

Research has also suggested a lack of screening and assessment tools for SUDs within VR services (Brickham et al., 2016; CSAT, 2011; Heinemann et al., 2014; Melvin et al., 2012; Sprong et al., 2014). The screening process allows the consumer to address their willingness and desire to gain competitive employment. Sprong, Upton, and Pappas (2012) suggested community rehabilitation programs with comprehensive vocational evaluation as a potential service to assist with the lack of screening processes. The Center for Substance Abuse Treatment (2000) also suggested the use of screening and assessment in conjunction to identify appropriate VR services for individuals with SUD.

SUDs are prevalent in the United States and exist as co-occurring conditions in many individuals with physical and psychological disabilities. Research has shown VR and employment-related services to be successful for individuals with SUD gaining competitive employment (Brickham et al., 2016; Lusk, 2018; Melvin et al., 2012; Petry et al., 2014). Continuing research should be completed to identify the success of VR services and obtain employment and retention as well as how screening and assessment can be used to identify individualized treatment outcomes.

Chapter Summary

When considering treatment approaches, the following questions may also be helpful. 1) How can we help understand our own biases and help clients with addiction issues? 2) What countertransference(s) may we experience with clients and addictions? 3) How can we help clients without enabling them, while maintaining empathy with them? 4) How can we maintain client accountability and volition, without being punitive? Along with counseling approaches, other community resources that may be helpful to clients with substance use issues include: *SAMHSA's Substance Abuse Treatment Locator* at www.findtreatment. samhsa.gov, the *SAMHSA National Helpline* (for locating drug and alcohol abuse treatment programs), and *Recovery.org*, among others.

While considering the various treatment practices and interventions for clients with substance use, abuse, and addiction, it is imperative that helpers stay continuously informed of varying practices. Research indicates that different clients work well with varying approaches and practices (APA, 2013). Only with knowledge of context, co-collaboration with clients, and application of varying practices can helpers most effectively administer appropriate practice for each client. Also, despite the treatment types utilized, it is important to maintain additive empathy for clients of all contexts and to help clients to facilitate their own change and self-validation. Substance use, abuse, or addiction may be a product of deeper interpersonal or intrapersonal issues, which may need to be addressed in counseling concurrently or thereafter, substance-related treatment, as well. Helpers are encouraged to use a plethora of empirically informed practices along with cultural inclusivity and client rapport to best help clients with substances abuse-related issues.

References

Brickham, D., Jeong Han, K., Gonzalez, R., & Rosenthal, D. (2016). Vocational outcomes of people with alcohol abuse/dependence who received state vocational rehabilitation services. *Journal of Vocational Rehabilitation, 45*(3), 267–279. doi:10.3233/JVR-160828

Brooks, F., & McHenry, B. (2015). *A contemporary approach to substance use disorders and addiction counseling* (2nd ed.). Alexandria, VA: American Counseling Association.

Center for Behavioral Health Statistics and Quality. (2015). *Behavioral health trends in the United States: Results from the 2014 National Survey on Drug Use and Health* (HHS Publication No. SMA 15-4927, NSDUH Series H-50). Retrieved from https://www.samhsa.gov/data/sites/default/files/NSDUH-FRR1-2014/NSDUH-FRR1-2014.pdf

Center for Substance Abuse Treatment. (1999). *Motivational interviewing as a counseling style.* Treatment Improvement Protocol (TIP) Series, No. 35. Rockville, MD: Substance Abuse and Mental Health Services Administration.

Center for Substance Abuse Treatment. (2000). *Integrating substance abuse treatment and vocational services.* Treatment Improvement Protocol (TIP) Series, No. 38. Rockville, MD: Substance Abuse and Mental Health Services Administration.

Chiesa, A., & Serretti, A. (2014). Are mindfulness-based interventions effective for substance use disorders? A systematic review of the evidence. *Substance Use & Misuse, 49*(5), 492–512.

Corey, G. (2016). *Theory and practice of group counseling* (9th ed.). Boston, MA: Cengage Learning.

Dobson, D., & Dobson, K. S. (2016). *Evidence-based practice of cognitive-behavioral therapy.* New York City, NY: Guilford Publications.

Glenn, M. K., Huber, M. J., Keferl, J., Wright-Bell, A., & Lane, T. (2008). Substance use disorders and vocational rehabilitation. VR Counselor's Desk Reference.

Grohol, J. (2018). 15 Common Cognitive Distortions. *Psych Central.* Retrieved May 13, 2018, from https://psychcentral.com/lib/15-common-cognitive-distortions/

Hassan, A., Bhatia, S. K., & Bhatia, S. C. (2017). Cognitive-behavioral therapy and other psychosocial interventions for substance use disorders. In S. C. Bhatia, F. Petty, and T. Gabel (Eds.), *Substance and nonsubstance related addiction disorder: Diagnosis and treatment* (pp. 227–242). Sharjah, UAE: Bentham Science.

Hayes, S. C., Strosahl, K. D., & Wilson, K. G. (2012). *Acceptance and commitment therapy.* New York, NY: Guilford Press.

Heinemann, A. W., Moore, D., Lazowski, L. E., Huber, M., & Semik, P. (2014). Benefits of substance use disorder screening on employment outcomes in state–federal vocational rehabilitation programs. *Rehabilitation Counseling Bulletin, 57*(3), 144–158. doi:10.1177/0034355213503908

Hollandsworth, J. G. (1990). *The physiology of psychological disorders*. New York, NY: Plenum Press.

Kegan, R. (1982). *The evolving self: Problem and process in human development*. Cambridge, MA: Harvard University Press.

Linehan, M. M. (1993). *Skills training manual for treating borderline personality disorder*. New York, NY: Guilford Press.

Lusk, S. L. (2018). Predictors of successful vocational rehabilitation closure among individuals with substance and alcohol use disorders: An analysis of rehabilitation services administration data 2010–2014. *Alcoholism Treatment Quarterly, 36*(2), 224–237.

Melvin, A., Davis, S., & Koch, D. S. (2012). Employment as a predictor of substance abuse treatment completion. *Journal of Rehabilitation, 78*, 31–37.

Miller, W. R., & Moyers, T. B. (2017). Motivational interviewing and the clinical science of Carl Rogers. *Journal of Consulting and Clinical Psychology, 85*(8), 757.

Miller, W. R., & Rollnick, S. (2002). *Motivational interviewing: Preparing people for change* (2nd ed.). New York: Guilford Press.

Pete, J. P., Diallo, A., Kaya, C., Brooks, J., Allen, M., Bezyak, J., & Fong, C. (2015). Vocational rehabilitation as a public health intervention for young African American men with substance use disorders. *Journal of Vocational Rehabilitation, 43*(2), 149–157. doi:10.3233/JVR-150764

Petry, N. M., Andrade, L. F., Rash, C. J., & Cherniack, M. G. (2014). Engaging in job-related activities is associated with reductions in employment problems and improvements in quality of life in substance abusing patients. *Psychology of Addictive Behaviors, 28*(1), 268.

Prochaska, J. O., & DiClemente, C. C. (1986). Toward a comprehensive model of change. In *Treating addictive behaviors* (pp. 3–27). New York, NY: Plenum.

Prochaska, J. O., DiClemente, C. C., & Norcross, J. C. (1992). In search of how people change: Applications to addictive behaviors. *American Psychologist, 47*(9), 1102.

Robins, C. J. Schmidt, H., & Linehan, M. M. (2004). Dialectical behavior therapy: Synthesizing radical acceptance with skillful means. In S. C. Hayes, V. M. Follette, & M. M. Linehan (Eds.), *Mindfulness and acceptance: Expanding the cognitive behavioral tradition* (pp. 30–44). New York, NY: Guilford Press.

Sharf, R. S. (2015). *Theories of psychotherapy and counseling: Concepts and cases* (6th ed.). Boston, MA: Cengage Learning.

Smout, M. F., Longo, M., Harrison, S., Minniti, R., Wickes, W., & White, J. M. (2010). Psychosocial treatment for methamphetamine use disorders: A preliminary randomized controlled trial of cognitive behavior therapy and acceptance and commitment therapy. *Substance Abuse, 31*(2), 98–107.

Sobell, L. C., & Sobell, M. B. (2011). *Group therapy with substance use disorders: A motivational cognitive behavioral approach*. New York, NY: Guilford Press.

Sprong, M. E., Dallas, B., Melvin, A., & Koch, D. S. (2014). Substance abuse and vocational rehabilitation: A survey of policies & procedures. *Journal of Rehabilitation, 80*(4), 4–9.

Sprong, M. E., Upton, T. D., & Pappas, M. (2012). Utilization of community rehabilitation programs: Screening for alcohol & drugs. *Journal of Rehabilitation, 78*(2), 13–19.

Chapter 9

Ethics and Assessment

Matthew E. Sprong
Hannah Barden
Hantac Chang
Deauna Froneberger

Key Terms: ethical principles, ethical standards, ethical decision-making model

Key Objectives: Students will learn how to apply an ethical decision-making model when faced with an ethical dilemma in assessment.

Assessment is a skill that many graduate-level programs include within the curriculum required for graduation. Usually, this is an entire course devoted to teaching students information related to that covered in Chapter 3 (e.g., standardization process, validity and reliability of instruments, direct and indirect observation), and students may be exposed to administering specific assessments. Ethics in assessment is an important topic that must be covered within these courses as counseling professionals are oftentimes presented with ethical conflicts and a well-prepared counseling professional will be able to choose the best course of action by utilizing code(s) of professional ethics, ethical decision-making models, and other procedures that assist in recognizing the benefits and issues with choosing a specific course of action. The purpose of this chapter is to provide information related to the role that ethics play in assessment.

Historical and Theoretical Background

Throughout the 20th century, there have been several examples of experiments and the scientific community now deems tests that have been conducted or used that as inappropriate. Unfortunately, at the time of these studies and projects, there was limited oversight or committees to review the potential harm that participants could experience. These studies, experiments, or assessments would likely not be approved in today's society as the risks would be seen as greater than the rewards. However, these studies, experiments, and assessments were essential in the inclusion of ethical assessment standards found in the professional code of ethics for different counseling disciplines.

Tuskegee Syphilis Study

The Tuskegee Syphilis experiment took place between 1932 and 1972 in Alabama on poor African American males. The study included 600 Black males (399 had syphilis, 201 did not have syphilis) and participants were told they were being treated for bad blood (Center for Disease Control and Prevention, 2017). The study was originally intended to last for 6 months. However, after nearly 40 years of the study, the public began to question the integrity of the study as the participants were never actually treated for syphilis, were never informed the true intent of the study, and did not provide informed consent. Furthermore, the study participants were never provided an opportunity to quit the study despite new highly effective treatment being released.

Milgram's Shock Therapy

Milgram's experiment involved focusing on conflict between obedience to authority and personal conscience in an attempt to explain why the World War II Nuremberg War Criminals may have complied with mass executions of Jews (Milgram, 1963). The defense for those on trial argued that they were just following orders from their superiors. Milgram designed an experiment that included a "learner" (actor in the study also called confederate) and the actual participant who would be assigned the role of "teacher." The teacher was instructed that he or she would read a series of questions and the learner would provide a response. After each question was read, if the learner was able to answer the question correctly, the teacher would read the next question. However, if the learner answered the question incorrectly, the teacher was instructed to provide a shock that was administered to the learner. The shock would increase in intensity as the learner would continue to provide incorrect responses. After each shock, the teacher would hear the learner yell (prerecorded tape) and as the intensity increased, the scream would increase. If the teacher questioned whether they should continue, the researcher would instruct them that the study must continue. At one point, the learner yelled "I have a heart condition," but several teachers (study participants) would continue with the shocks. On the shock generator, the shock switches toward the more intense shocks indicated (dangerous) and at one point the screams stopped (closer to 450 volts of electricity).

Stanford Prison Experiment

The Stanford Prison Experiment was conducted in 1971 by a Psychologist named Philip Zimbardo with the primary goal of evaluating the effects of perceived power. Specifically, Zimbardo and his colleagues were interested in examining the struggle between prisoners and prison officers (Zimbardo, 1971). Individuals who agreed to participate in the study were randomly assigned to play the role of either a prison guard or a prison inmate. Those assigned to play the prison inmates were officially arrested by the local police department and were transported to a "prison" that was built in the basement of the Psychology department at Stanford and were forced to wear prison garments. The participants who were selected as the prison guards sat in an orientation the day before the experiment where they were instructed not to physically harm the "prisoners" or withhold food or drink, but could create feelings of boredom, a sense of fear to some degree, create a notion of arbitrariness that their life is completely controlled by the prison guards, and the "prisoners" have no privacy. After the second day of the study, it became apparent that prisoners blockaded their cell door with their beds in an attempt to revolt against the prison guards. Interestingly, the prison guards volunteered to work extra shifts and decided to set up a privilege cell for prisoners who did not engage in the revolt, which included "higher quality" meals. The prison guards forced some prisoners to be naked as punishment and several other guards began to engage in other cruel acts. After 6 days, the experiment was stopped as the study was getting out of hand. One study participant began to have severe psychological symptoms and some of the professionals who were aware of the study began to question the morality of the study.

Development of Standards in Assessment/Research

There are several other unethical projects that have been conducted throughout history. For example, Project MkUltra secret CIA project (1953–1973) that included experiments that was conducted on several U.S. citizens in an attempt to assess the potential use of lysergic acid diethylamide (LSD) and other drugs for mind control techniques, without consent of participants. Another example includes the Willowbrook Experiments from 1956 to 1970 in which children with developmental disabilities were intentionally given hepatitis in an attempt to track the development of the viral infection. The several aforementioned research projects are well-known examples that are commonly used in classes that discuss ethics in research. Due to the nature of the issues that were identified in all of these projects, society determined there needed to be standards established in order to prevent these issues from continuing. In assessment, the rewards should always outweigh the risks associated with participation, and clients should be allowed to consent to participate in the assessment. In almost every discipline where professionals administer assessments, there are likely ethical standards that were developed by the profession that dictates how assessments should be administered, along with other vital information for counseling professionals to consider.

Ethics Defined

The concept of "Ethics" in the helping professions (e.g., psychology, counseling, rehabilitation counseling) was adopted in Psychology in the late 1930s to handle complaints on an informal basis (Pope & Vetter, 1992; Rich, 1952). As Van Hoose and Kottler (1985) stated, "ethics is concerned with questions that have no ultimate answers, yet are important to planning one's life, justifying one's activities, and deciding what one ought to do" (p. 3). However, despite the interpretative nature of ethics, the American Psychological Association continued to establish a set of ethical standards to help guide the profession and professionals working within the profession. As Pope and Vetter stated, in 1947, a formal code was recommended and developed using a "task force" consisting of psychological experts. The code included scenarios that displayed ethical-related issues and dilemmas, and in 1959 the code of professional ethics was revised and adopted on a trial bases (American Psychological Association, 1953; Pope & Vetter, 1992). The code of ethics has been continuously revised in years thereafter and has led to the development of professional code of ethics in other helping professions (e.g., rehabilitation counseling, mental health counseling).

The process of developing professional codes of ethics is somewhat similar across disciplines. Revisions generally occur after forming an ethical task force, which consists of scholars within the profession (e.g., educators, professionals working in the field). The ethical task force will conduct critical incident studies (CIS) that enable measurement of current ethical violations and allow the task force to modify ethical standards to reduce ethical violations or decide if more explanation is needed to provide guidance to professionals applying the code. In addition to CIS, ethical task forces will update the professional code of ethics based on professional/societal demands or factors related to cultural changes and other scientific-based studies. In some instances, the ethical task force may use other professionals to provide feedback related to the newly developed/modified ethical standards. In addition to the CIS, the ethical task force may consider peer-reviewed journal article publications related to ethics to make recommendations to modify the ethical codes to satisfy these needs. Ethics are generally developed with the intention of respecting human rights and dignity, while at the same time ensuring the integrity of all professional relationships. A counseling professional who is faced with an ethical dilemma should be able to review the standards provided by his or her profession and be provided guidance when determining how to proceed. Furthermore, the code also enhances the quality of professional knowledge and its application to increase effectiveness.

Ethical Principles

There are six ethical principles that most helping profession outline within the discipline's code of professional ethics, including (1) autonomy, (2) beneficence, (3) non-maleficence, (4) fidelity, (5) justice, and (6) veracity. The principle of *autonomy* is related to the client being included in the decision-making process and having the right to choose the best course of action. In treatment planning, the client would have the opportunity to assist in the development of treatment goals. The client who is included in the treatment planning process is likely to take more initiative in completing treatment goals, and the client and counseling professional can develop treatment goals that are realistic (see Chapter 10). The counseling professional should assist the client in understanding the strengths and limitations of making decisions by providing all information so that the client can fully understand how the decisions will impact factors associated with the client (Corey, Corey, & Callanan, 2011). The principle of *beneficence* and *non-maleficence* involves the counseling professional striving to benefit the client with whom he or she works with while doing no harm to the client (American Psychological Association, 2002). *Beneficence* refers to the notion of "doing good" to the client and taking action to improve the situation of others (LaFollette & Persson, 2013). This includes safeguarding the welfare of the client and the rights of all clients that the counseling professional works with. Counseling professionals should resolve conflicts that occur with a careful observation of how choosing a course of action might increase or decrease harm to the client. Furthermore, counseling professionals should be aware of their own physical and psychological health because this could negatively impact the clients they work with if the health begins to deteriorate. This is accomplished by regularly engaging in professional development, conducting systematic monitoring of practice and outcomes, and practicing continuous self-assessment to determine if personal values are limiting service delivery (Cottone & Tarvydas., 2007). The principle of *Fidelity* refers to the counseling professional establishing a therapeutic relationship with the client that is centered on trust and non-judgment (Sprong, Cioe, Yalamanchili, & McDermott, 2015). This includes staying current on evidence-based practices and incorporating these into service delivery. Furthermore, this ethical principle involves being faithful, loyal, truthful, and being respectful to the client, while agreeing to keep promises made to the client. The principle of *Justice* recognizes that fairness to all clients to access and benefit from a counseling professional that is impartial emphasizes equality among clients, and practices reciprocity (treat people how you wish to be treated). Counseling professionals offer everyone the same opportunities and do not withhold opportunities for specific clients. *Veracity* is the principle of truth telling, which is essential to honor the person's autonomy (Welfel, 2012). Welfel suggested that truth telling is violated by the act of lying or providing erroneous information to the client, as well as by omitting all or some portions of the truth. Therefore, violating this ethical principle can eliminate or reduce a client's right to make decisions related to the rehabilitation plan by withholding or providing false information to the client. Even with the ethical principles to guide counseling professionals' service delivery, often there are times when conflict resolution and negotiation strategies are needed (e.g., the expectations and perceptions of the counselor and client are different) when developing treatment goals.

Ethics in Assessment

Counseling professionals who assist clients who have substance-related disorders or substance use barriers come from several different disciplines (e.g., Rehabilitation Counseling, Mental Health Counseling, Psychology, Social Work, Substance Abuse Counseling). Each code of professional ethics for these different disciplines provides guidance on the appropriate procedures of conducting testing and information on what competencies the counseling professional must consider when involved in the assessment process.

Despite different counseling organizations releasing their version of ethical standards, there are several similarities between the sections on assessment. For example, each code of professional ethics provides guidance related to competence use and interpreting the assessment results, diagnosing of mental disorders, confidentiality of scores and release of information, and assessment administration. There are other categories within each ethical code. The counseling professional should evaluate these sections prior to engaging in the assessment process, as the counseling professional is bound by the license or certification they hold. For example, if a substance abuse counselor was a licensed clinical professional counselor (LCPC), he or she needs to review the American Counseling Association's code of professional ethics. However, some states have their own certification to practice substance abuse counseling (e.g., State of Illinois). If certified in that specific state, their code of professional ethics takes precedence. However, some code of professional ethics were developed by considering other counseling professions as a mechanism to avoid conflict if a counseling professional has several certifications and licenses. Despite several similarities and some differences between the ethical standards in each discipline, informed consent, privacy, and confidentiality, and user qualifications are almost identical in the meaning behind the description in these specific ethical standards.

Informed Consent, Privacy, and Confidentiality

Informed consent is the "process of communication whereby a client is enabled to make an informed and voluntary decision about accepting or declining treatment and/or services provided by an agency" (Cottone & Tarvydas, 2007). Informed consent consists of four components, including the client must be (1) competent and have decision-making capacity; (2) the counseling professional and agency must disclose all information in its entirety related to the risks, benefits, and alternatives to treatment; (3) the client must be able to understand this information; and (4) the client must provide voluntary consent, which protects the client from coercion and undue influence (Sprong et al., 2015). Informed consent must be provided prior to assessment, as counselors should explain the nature, purpose of assessment, and the use of the results to potential recipients, including the clients, should be presented in a format that is most conducive to the client, or other legally authorized persons. Prior to assessment, the counseling professional must consider the welfare of the client. With the release of data to qualified personnel, the counseling has to obtain a release of information consent identified by the client or the client's legal representative. Such data are released only to persons recognized by counseling professionals as qualitied to interpret the data (ACA, 2014, Section E).

User Qualifications

User qualifications in testing is essential in the process of determining whether a counseling professional has the knowledge, skills, and abilities to properly administer a test. The Standards for Educational and Psychological Testing (published by the American Educational Research Association) developed qualification levels that provide required education and knowledge prior to purchasing a test to use. For example, a psychological intelligence test is going to require the user to have a certain level of education or professional oversight (e.g., doctorate degree, license) to purchase and use the test. Each test that is sold should have a qualification level associated with it, so a counseling professional will be aware of whether he or she can administer the test or need the assistance of another professional. It should also be noted that although a counseling professional might meet the qualifications to purchase and administer the test, the counseling professional should be training on the administration of each test they use. For example, they should thoroughly review the test manual so that they follow the standardization process established by the test developers (see Chapter 3).

Qualification Level	Education	Other Requirements
Qualification A	No special qualifications to purchase these products	
Qualification B	Master's degree in psychology, education, occupational therapy, social work, counseling, or closely related field (must have formal training in ethical administration, scoring, and interpretation of clinical assessment)	Certification by or full active membership in a professional organization that requires training and experience in the relevant area of assessment or A degree or license to practice in the healthcare or allied healthcare field or Formal, supervised experience, and/or educational/formal training in ethical administration, scoring, and interpretation of clinical assessment
Qualification C	Doctorate degree in psychology, education, or closely related field (must have formal training in ethical administration, scoring, and interpretation of clinical assessment)	Licensure or Certification to practice in the individual's state in a field related to the purchase or Certification by or full active membership in a professional organization that requires training and experience in the relevant area of assessment

Note: The counseling professional should review the specific requirements for qualification levels of a test. We summarized the qualifications for purposes of the table from Drummond and Jones (2010).

Ethical Decision-Making Model

There are several decision-making models that have been developed to assist counseling professionals in the ethical decision-making process. An ethical decision-making model is beneficial when a counseling professional is faced with an ethical dilemma that where violating an ethical principle or standard could hurt the client. Prior to engaging in the ethical decision-making process to resolve an ethical dilemma, a counseling professional must first determine whether there is conflict between personal and professional values that are influencing the conflict. Kinnier (1995) provide a framework for counseling professionals to internalize potential conflict and practice conflict resolution between personal and the profession's values. The counseling professional should always abide by the professional standards as there was an ethics team that was established to develop or modify the ethical standards in place. Once the counseling professional determines that the conflict is purely with the professional values (e.g., two ethical principles), the counseling professional must apply the ethical decision-making model. Usually, models follow a similar pattern in terms of the steps of determining the best course of action, including (as cited in Sprong et al., 2015, Cottone & Tarvydas, 2007)):

1. Identification of the problem,
2. Identification of the potential solutions,
3. Review of the ethical code for guidance,
4. Project and assess the potential consequences for each solution,
5. Solicit feedback from others,
6. Select and implement a course of action,
7. Reflect on the decision and consequences

In the model listed above, the counseling professional is generally brainstorming all of the problems that he or she is presented with, and all of the potential courses of action that are available. Additionally, the counseling professional is capable of detecting the benefits and limitations of selecting each course of action and should use the course of action with the least amount of risk.

Case Scenario

Natalie is currently employed as a counseling professional at a CARF-accredited residential treatment facility for individuals with substance-related disorders that meet criteria for Level 3 care. She is primarily responsible for providing case management and counseling services to her clients. Additionally, she is well skilled in administering several different assessments and is an expert on interpreting the test results and incorporating them into a report. Natalie's co-worker and supervisor, Amanda, works with the remaining clients at the agency. Natalie and Amanda have formed a friendship throughout the past 6 years, as both were a part of the same Master's degree cohort. They graduated at the top of their class, studied for and passed National Certification Examination in order to obtain state licensure, and both became employed by the same agency at the same time.

On one social occasion, Amanda, Natalie, and a few other friends were out eating dinner. They were celebrating Natalie's award at work for most successful case closures in a 5-year period. Amanda and Natalie were reminiscing about graduate school. During the conversation, Natalie turned to Amanda with a grin on her face and informed Amanda that she lost his credential as a LCPC because she failed to complete the continuing education (CEU) requirements. Amanda presumed that Natalie was joking around since she was always well organized and graduated at the top of their class. Amanda later came to the realization that Natalie was not following standardized protocols on the assessments she has been administering and some of the data may have been fabricated. When Amanda confronted Natalie regarding this issue, Natalie said that the way she administered tests were fine and that Amanda was being too critical.

Application of Ethical Decision-Making Model

As may be evident by the above case scenario, there are several apparent issues that need to be addressed. The first step of the ethical decision-making model is identification of the problem. Natalie has been misrepresenting her credentials to the clients that she serves, and to third-party reimbursement companies, and potentially clients paying out of pocket. A license designation is awarded to those who demonstrate certain competencies and is a way to regulate professionals. Natalie has not completed her CEU units which provide education related to evidence-based best practices, as well as assist her in improving her counseling skills. Those are a few of the apparent problems from the case study but there may be other issues present. There are several solutions that Amanda can take to solve the problem. She can report this to the clients, the third-party reimbursement companies, and to the administrator at the agency they are both employed. Furthermore, she could report it to the state regulatory agency so that Natalie would be unable to get licensed in the future due to unethical practices. There are several ethical standards that would address this issue. An example from the American Counseling Association might include:

C.2.c. Qualified for Employment: Counselors accept employment only for positions for which they are qualified given their education, training, supervised experience, state and national professional credentials, and appropriate professional experience. Counselors hire for professional counseling positions only individuals who are qualified and competent for those positions.

C.2.f. Continuing Education: Counselors recognize the need for CEU to acquire and maintain a reasonable level of awareness of current scientific and professional information in their fields of activity. Counselors maintain their competence in the skills they use, are open to new procedures, and remain informed regarding best practices for working with diverse populations.

A requirement to work at the agency is to be an LCPC. Natalie was misrepresenting her professional credentials and is still employed at the agency. Natalie has not completed CEU units that are not only required for her licensure but also to stay informed on best practices and maintain her level of competency in counseling areas. Although what Amanda needs to do might seem obvious, there are some consequences that come into play. Natalie has a high success rate in terms of clients completing services. Additionally, if Natalie was not following the standardized protocols of the test she administered, the scores may be deemed as inaccurate, which could lead to litigation, the agency losing their accreditation to practice, and several clients who are served by this agency may lose treatment options as a result of the agency closing. It will be vital for Amanda to reaching out to other professional colleagues to ascertain their thoughts and professional opinions on how to handle the issue at hand. Amanda has at least two options of how to continue, including (1) do and say nothing related to Natalie's licensure and lack of assessment administration integrity, or (2) report Natalie.

Activity

Directions: Using the brief scenario below, implement the ethical decision-making model as comprehensively as possible. For the code of professional ethics portion, use the code established by your discipline, but also consider using the code of ethics from another discipline. This process will assist you in becoming familiar with how to navigate through the code of ethics and you will learn how to apply different ethical standards depending on the situation you are faced with.

A client named Maverick has been referred to your agency for an evaluation to assess for a substance-related disorder, as well as, appropriate level of care that would assist in reducing significant challenges that Maverick is facing. You are the counseling professional who will be conducting a comprehensive assessment on Maverick to assess what services may be most appropriate. Your program director informs you that the agency needs to increase the clients that they serve so that it can maintain payroll and operating costs. She informs you that Maverick will need an assessment that demonstrates the need for Residential Care so that he can receive treatment at this agency. Your program director informs you that the agency will need to terminate staff and counseling professionals if more clients are not served. Your best friend, who is also an employee at the agency, became the primary source of income as her husband lost his job several months ago and now has cancer. Needless to say, he needs treatment and the only insurance plan they can afford is through her work at the agency. Additionally, the agency is the closest residential treatment facility within hundreds of miles.

Chapter Summary

Counseling professionals must be aware of the implications that their decisions can have in the counseling process. Continuously reviewing the code of professional ethics is essential if counseling professionals wish to practice appropriately and make accurate decisions. Oftentimes, counseling professionals will be faced with ethical dilemmas that will need to be evaluated so that the best course of action can be provided.

Therefore, this chapter provided an example of one ethical decision-making model that counseling professionals could use in order to choose the best course of action. Of course, we recommend reviewing the other ethical decision-making models and practicing these so that future counseling professionals can become familiar with the current code of ethics and how to explore the benefits and limitations of choosing one option over another.

References

American Counseling Association (ACA). (2014). ACA code of ethics. Retrieved from http://www.counseling.org/resources/aca-code-of-ethics.pdf

American Psychological Association. (1953). *Ethical standards of psychologists.* Washington, DC: Author.

American Psychological Association (APA). (2002). Ethical principles of psychologists and code of conduct. Retrieved from http://www.apa.org/ethics/code/ethics-code-2017.pdf

American Psychological Association. (2016). Ethical principles of psychologists and code of conduct. Retrieved from http://www.apa.org/ethics/code/

Center for Disease Control and Prevention. (2017). U.S. Public Health Service Syphilis Study at Tuskegee. Retrieved from https://www.cdc.gov/tuskegee/timeline.htm

Commission on Rehabilitation Counselor Certification. (2017). *Code of professional ethics for rehabilitation counselors.* Schaumburg, IL: Author.

Corey, G., Corey, M. S., & Callanan, P. (2011). *Issues and ethics in the helping profession* (8th ed.). Pacific Grove, CA: Brooks/Cole.

Cottone, R. R., & Tarvydas, V. M. (2007). *Counseling ethics and decision making* (3rd ed.). Upper Saddle River, NJ: Pearson Education Inc.

Drummond, R., & Jones, K. (2010). *Assessment procedures for counselors and helping professionals* (7th ed.). Upper Saddle River, NJ: Pearson.

Kinnier, R. T. (1995). A reconceptualization of values clarification: Values conflict resolution. *Journal of Counseling & Development, 74*(1), 18–24.

LaFollette, H., & Persson, I. (2013). *The Blackwell guide to ethical theory* (2nd ed.). Hoboken, NJ: John Wiley & Sons.

Milgram, S. (1963). Behavioral study of obedience. *The Journal of Abnormal and Social Psychology, 67*(4), 371–378.

Pope, K. S., & Vetter, V. A. (1992). Ethical dilemmas encountered by members of the American Psychological Association: A national survey. *American Psychologist, 47*(3), 397–411.

Rich, G. J. (1952). A new code of ethics is needed. *American Psychologist, 7,* 440–441.

Sprong, M. E., Cioe, N., Yalamanchili, P., & McDermott, A., (2015). Principles of ethics. In J. Stano (Ed.), *Ethics in rehabilitation counseling: A case study approach.* Osage Beech, MO: Aspen Professional Services.

Van Hoose, W. H., & Kottler, J. A. (1985). *Ethical and legal issues in counseling and psychotherapy* (2nd ed.). San Francisco, CA: Jossey Bass.

Welfel, E. R. (2012). *Ethics in counseling & psychotherapy: Standards, research, and emerging issues.* Belmont, CA: Brooks/Cole.

Zimbardo, P. (1971). *The Stanford prison experiment: A simulation study of the psychology of imprisonment.* [Pdf] Stanford: Stanford University, Stanford Digital Repository.

Chapter 10

Utilization of Assessment Information in Treatment Plan Development

Matthew E. Sprong

Heaven Hollender

Key Terms: treatment planning, establishing treatment goals, case conceptualization, disability considerations, S.M.A.R.T. goals

Key Objectives: Students will be able to apply information covered in other chapters to develop specific and measurable goals within their treatment plans.

Introduction to Treatment Planning

Treatment planning is an essential component to assist a counseling professional in providing therapeutic services to people who have drug and alcohol obstacles. The goal of treatment is to (a) reduce substance use or achieve a substance-free life, (b) maximize multiple aspects of life functioning, and (c) prevent or reduce the frequency and severity of relapse (Schuckit, 1994). A treatment plan should be developed to assist the client in eliminating or reducing barriers that prevent the individual from having a high quality of life (subjective to the client) and assist in eliminating problems that the client brings to the counseling process (Substance Abuse Mental Health Services Administration, 2009a). The counseling professional and client periodically review the treatment plan, as it can inform both of whether the client is (1) improving or getting better, (2) declining or getting worse, or (3) is stagnant in their treatment recovery (staying the same). There are several factors that might influence why a client is not improving. For example, the timeline of when the goals should be completed may not be realistic, the goals may not be specific enough, the client may not have the tools required to complete the goal. The counseling professional should work with the client in order to identify the barrier to goal attainment. The purpose of this chapter is to discuss the process of treatment plan development by incorporating the assessment information discussed in the previous chapters.

Treatment Plan Development

In order to develop an appropriate treatment plan, a counseling professional must gather vital information about the client-seeking services. If the level of care has already been determined for the client, then there should be information available for the counseling professional to review. For example, there are six dimensions established by Mee-Lee (2013), including (1) acute intoxication and/or withdrawal potential; (2) biomedical conditions and complications; (3) emotional, behavioral, and cognitive conditions and complications; (4) readiness to change; (5) relapse, continued use, continued problem potential; and (6) recovery environment. To establish the appropriate level of care for the individual, there needs to be documented evidence for each dimension aforementioned. As discussed in Chapter 3, administering a valid and reliable instrument to the client to ascertain information related to problems the client has can provide more specific information related to the severity level. For example, if the client presents other psychological-related barriers, a test that measures possible psychiatric diagnoses would be beneficial to assist in isolating symptoms associated with specific diagnoses. Once this is completed, further evaluation can be conducted to determine if in fact the symptoms lead to a clinical diagnosis.

Essentially, a counseling professional will ascertain all of the assessment information gathered about a client, and collaboratively work with the client to define the problem(s) or barriers that are preventing the client from achieving his or her goals. A treatment plan will include a timeline for treatment progress, identifying major treatment goals, and noting important milestones and objectives. Although substance users are primarily in treatment for drugs and/or alcohol, a treatment plan must address barriers such as (a) medical/biological, (b) social, (c) spiritual, (d) vocational, and (e) psychological. Oftentimes, barriers in these areas can lead to the use of substances to avoid or escape the harmful effects of the symptoms associated with these barriers.

It is important that the client is involved in the treatment plan development process, as it will increase the likelihood that the client will be a willing participant in the treatment program, and together the counseling professional and client can establish realistic goals. After comprehensively discussing the presenting issues that the client brings to treatment, a counseling professional can request that the client develop some goals they might have for treatment. Remember, a client may not be as experienced in goal-writing so it is important for the counseling professional to be open-minded when presented with the client goals. Having the client come up with goals helps portray that the client is taking ownership of his or her treatment recovery process and leads to the next step of case conceptualization.

Case Conceptualization

Prior to developing a treatment plan, a case conceptualization may be beneficial because it allows for a counseling professional to develop an overall depiction of the client's overall situation. A case conceptualization is a report that is based on information gathered, organized, and assessed to provide an explanation of a client's behavior (Gilmore, Seirup, & Rubinstein, 2011). Furthermore, case conceptualization is a "bridge between client diagnosis or problem and specific treatments to be implemented" (Sommers-Flanagan & Sommers-Flanagan, 2015, p. 347). Counseling professionals during the clinical interview must look for emotional, stated, nonverbal, and behavioral information that will assist in formulating the picture of the client's experience and this can lead to collaboration when developing goals with the client. Case conceptualization may feel overwhelming for the new counseling professional. However, the process below may be helpful in assisting a counseling professional regardless of experience in fully formulating a case (Eells, 2015):

1. Listen to the client's story/presenting problem
2. Gather information about how the client perceives his/her world
3. Obtain demographic information
4. Explore social, historical, and cultural context
5. Assess client's strengths, coping skills
6. Assess for risk; create problem list
7. Diagnose
8. Apply theoretical orientation and hypothesize about the nature of the problem
9. Develop goals
10. Plan interventions

A counseling professional who can learn to engage in case conceptualization can identify the necessary steps that might be needed to assist a client in pursuing his or her long-term goal. For example, suppose a client named Bryan has the long-term goal of reducing his anger outbursts. A counseling professional should listen to issues related to anger outbursts that the client experiences. One way to accomplish this goal is to learn positive coping skills. Some areas that the counseling professional should consider exploring within a counseling session might include identifying a specific moment in time when the client had an anger outburst (examining the cognitive and affective aspects of the situation). Cognitive behavioral theory outlines three areas that should be explored with a client in order to process irrational thinking, including the cognitive (thought), affect (emotion), and situational (behavioral).

Now pretend that Bryan is discussing a recent event with his counseling professional where he was involved in a verbal altercation with a family member at a recent holiday party. It might be helpful for Bryan to completely describe the situation so that the counseling professional can understand the context of the situation. What led to the verbal altercation? At what point was Bryan getting upset? Who else was present? What was Bryan thinking prior to the verbal altercation? What was Bryan thinking after the verbal altercation? How long after the verbal altercation did Bryan's anger begin to decrease? These are examples of questions that can assist a counseling professional in exploring previous events related to Bryan's goal.

The treatment plan can include specific steps to assist the counseling professional in terms of thoroughly exploring previous coping skills that were used in the past and exploring current coping skills as they are used in practice. In the example below, we are ascertaining information from Bryan throughout his counseling sessions to assist him in reaching one of his goals of reducing his anger outbursts.

Long-term goal #1: Help Bryan learn positive coping skills that his parents neglected to teach him during his childhood. This will be completed by 5/25/xx.

> **Short-term goal/objective #1:** Bryan will learn appropriate coping skills by 4/11/xx.

> > **Intervention/Action step #1:** Bryan will develop a list of coping skills that he has attempted to use in the past. This will be completed on 4/4/xx.

> > **Intervention/Action step #2:** Bryan will describe the situation/event of each coping skills he had indicated that he has used. Bryan will describe his cognition, affect, and behavior regarding the situation/event. This will be completed on 4/4/xx.

> > **Intervention/Action step #3:** After describing each situation/event, Bryan will state what coping skill he used and rate how effective each coping skill was on a scale of 1–7 (1 = not effective, 7 = very effective) with regard to reducing his anger. This will be completed on 4/4/xx.

> > **Intervention/Action step #4:** Bryan will review a list of examples of appropriate coping skills provided by the counselor and describe how the coping skills on the list the counselor provided are different than the coping skills that he has attempted in the past. This will be completed by 4/11/xx.

> > **Intervention/Action step #5:** Bryan will review a list of appropriate coping skills provided by the counselor and select or develop 10 coping skills that he will use during the next few weeks. This will be completed by 4/11/xx.

In the example treatment plan for Bryan shown above, the first short-term goal is to assist Bryan in learning appropriate coping skills. Although there is flexibility in determining how to proceed with a client, it may be beneficial to first explore how long Bryan has had episodes of anger, and has he used any coping skills in the past. After examining each action step of short-term goal 1, it should become evident that there is a flow in terms of assisting Bryan in examining what was used in the past, what could be used in the future, and determining which coping skills might be most helpful. If Bryan were provided a list of 20 coping skills and attempted to use three or four at the same time, it would be difficult to identify what was the most effective and what was not.

Short-term goal 2 (see below) is related to Bryan demonstrating appropriate coping skills. Oftentimes, a counseling professional will begin with short-term goal 2, rather than first determining if the client understands how to effectively use coping skills and being able to process how these coping skills might be used. After Bryan selects a few positive coping skills to try over the next few weeks, Bryan will have the opportunity to actually attempt to employ these in practice.

Short-term goal/objective #2: Bryan will demonstrate how to use appropriate coping skills by 5/25/xx.

Intervention/Action step #1: From the list of coping skills that Bryan has developed, he will select two coping skills to use in the next few weeks. This will be completed by 4/11/xx.

Intervention/Action step #2: After getting into an argument, Bryan will process the situation/event by writing a short narrative of what happened, what his thoughts, emotions, and behaviors were regarding the event. This will be completed by 4/18/xx.

Intervention/Action step #3: Bryan will use one of the two selected coping mechanisms after he gets in an argument with his girlfriend (trial 1). He will indicate how many minutes after the initial argument did his anger reduce and rate how effective each coping skill was on a scale of 1–7 (1 = not effective, 7 = very effective) at reducing his anger. This will be completed by 4/18/xx.

Intervention/Action step #4: Bryan will continue to use the most effective coping mechanism from (trial 1) and select one new coping mechanism from the list. This will be completed on 4/18/xx.

Intervention/Action step #5: Bryan will use one of the two selected coping mechanisms after he gets in an argument with his girlfriend. He will indicate how many minutes after the initial argument did his anger reduce and rate how effective each coping skill was on a scale of 1–7 (1 = not effective, 7 = very effective) at reducing his anger. This will be completed by 4/25/xx.

As displayed above, there are several action steps within each short-term goal that can provide a visual of how a client might progress in meeting a treatment goal. Sometimes, several interventions/action steps can be completed within the same counseling session (e.g., short-term goal one, action step(s) 1 and 2), and sometimes the interventions are completed over several counseling sessions.

Development of Goals and Action Steps/Objectives

Goal-writing is a skill that can take a counseling professional significant practice to accomplish. Goal setting is an essential part and central to a treatment plan, and should be (Bovend'Eerdt, Botell, & Wade, 2009, p. 353):

1. Individualized to a particular client
2. Allow accurate, unambiguous determination of goal achievement
3. Are flexible enough to cover most situations

In addition to the three bullet points provided above, treatment goals should be written in a positive manner, and be developed collaboratively with the client. Within the counseling field, there has been greater emphasis that counseling professionals develop S.M.A.R.T. goals within their treatment plan. These types of goals stand for specific (S), measurable (M), attainable (A), realistic or results-oriented (R), and Time specific (T). Aligning with this framework will provide more specificity in terms of (1) the services to be provided (e.g., group, individual, family, support groups), (2) the services to be obtained from specific providers, (3) the frequency of treatment, (4) delineate termination criteria, (5) include all domains of functional assessment as needed, and (6) specific goals and objectives. The S.M.A.R.T. framework also assists in making the treatment goals behaviorally oriented and is aimed at client improvement. The short-term goals/objectives are the activities that must be accomplished to reach the short-term goal, directly measurable, unique to the client, concise and precise, and comprehensive. The action steps are the tasks that are needed to carry out or reach objectives.

Case Scenario #1:

Bryan is receiving counseling services at an outpatient facility as required from a court mandate due to a driving under the influence (DUI) charge and his previous history with several DUI charges. During his individualized counseling session, Bryan disclosed that he has had difficulty finding employment because he never completed the 12th grade and has no high school diploma. He stated that he has had previous employment, but due to the increase in computerized equipment, his employment was terminated. Bryan and his counselor developed a goal to assist Bryan in obtaining his general education degree (GED) from his local college:

Long-term goal #1: Bryan will obtain his 12th grade GED by 6/5/xx.

   Short-term goal/objective #1: Bryan will go to Illinois Valley Community College on the community bus to get a GED application by 3/5/xx.

      Intervention/Action step #1: Bryan will get a bus schedule from the front desk in the lobby and review plans for taking the community bus with his counselor today.

      Intervention/Action step #1: Bryan will get a bus pass from the agency transportation department tomorrow.

   Short-term goal/objective #2: Bryan will complete the application and review it with his counselor on 3/10/xx.

      Intervention/Action step #1: Following a successful review, Bryan will mail his application to Illinois Valley Community College on 3/10/xx.

Case Scenario #2:

Long-term goal #1: Bryan will quit using drugs.

Short-term goal/objective #1: Bryan will avoid all triggers.

Intervention/Action step #1: Bryan will find new friends

Intervention/Action step #1: Bryan will ignore his old friends who use drugs.

As displayed above, we have two separate scenarios. In the first scenario, Bryan had a specific goal of obtaining his 12th-grade GED by a specific date. If Bryan is unable to complete the specific short-term goals/objectives, the counseling professional is able to review with Bryan as to the potential barriers that prevented him from achieving his short-term goals. In the second scenario, there is a lot of information missing. For example, when does Bryan need to complete the goal by? A treatment goal with action steps that are time specific assists a counseling professional in evaluating effort. Another issue with case scenario 2, what does avoid all trigger mean? How might Bryan quit using drugs? The treatment goal needs to be more specific.

Although case scenario 1 is more specific than case scenario 2, additional short-term goals/objectives and action steps can be included. Some additional considerations might be studying for the examination, taking the examination, reviewing results of the examination with his counselor. As provided earlier in the chapter, Bryan wanted assistance with his anger outbursts and several objectives and action steps were provided. As just demonstrated, the more specific the goal becomes, the easier it will become when evaluating why the goal was completed or why it did not get completed. Please consider the following mini-activity:

Mini-activity:

1. After learning about the S.M.A.R.T framework, would you claim that this part of Bryan's treatment plan is compliant with this framework?
2. What specifically do you notice that is problematic?
3. Consider applying the S.M.A.R.T. framework.

Utilization Review Process

Once a treatment plan has been established, a counseling professional and client can begin the process of achieving the client's short-term and long-term goals. This will involve periodic review of the treatment goals to determine if goals are being met. As aforementioned, a treatment plan informs us if the client is (1) improving or getting better, (2) declining or getting worse, or (3) is stagnant in their treatment recovery (staying the same). If the agency that the counseling professional is employed by has an accreditation agency (e.g., Commission on Accreditation of Rehabilitation Facilities [CARF], Joint Commission) that provide standards that the agency must abide by, guidance related to treatment review will likely be provided. For example, agencies accredited by the CARF require a weekly review with the client and a monthly review with the treatment team members (2018). Additionally, the counseling professional should become familiar with state legislation related to the utilization process, as some states provide specific details as to the frequency that a treatment plan must be reviewed. For example, some state Medicaid programs (e.g., Vermont) may mandate review every 15 days for adults/30 days for adolescents (Donsel, 2014).

Evaluating Effectiveness of Goals, Continuing Care, and Treatment Termination

During the review process, a counseling professional can determine how effective treatment has been for the client attempting to complete treatment goals. If goals are developed using the S.M.A.R.T. framework, the counseling professional can mark all of the short-term objectives/goals that were completed in the time frame specified and those that were not. A conversation should follow with the client to determine if the time frame for each action step was realistic, if other challenges prevented the accomplishment of the action step, or if motivation was a factor. For example, in the case scenario above, Bryan was planning on obtaining his 12th-grade GED by 6/5/xx. The first short-term goal/objective was for Bryan to go to the local college to obtain a GED application. The intervention/action steps provided were ordered in a step-by-step manner so that the likelihood of accomplishing the goal was successful. For example, Bryan was going to get a bus schedule from the front desk and review it with his counselor. The next step was for Bryan to return to the agency the following day to obtain a bus pass. If Bryan was unable to accomplish this action step, then he would be unable to successfully complete the short-term goal/objective. Some issues that may have prevented Bryan from accomplishing this action step could include (a) lack of transportation to return to the agency the following day, (b) family emergency, (c) Bryan relapsed, (d) Bryan forgot to return the following day for a bus pass, (e) the agency ran out of bus passes. Any of these possibilities might have occurred and the counseling professional can discuss the barriers that prevented Bryan from completing this task. This needs to be accomplished prior to Bryan obtaining his GED application form.

Oftentimes, continuing care for substance use treatment will heavily involve completing treatment goals. For example, individuals who are court mandated through drug courts will often have a probation officer who periodically checks in with the client's counseling professional. If treatment goals are consistently not being met, or if the client is not demonstrating the motivation to complete treatment, the probation officer might suggest that the client is terminated from treatment unsuccessfully, and the drug court may recommend jail time. The counseling professional may be able to verbalize his or her opinion regarding termination or continued treatment. It is important for the counseling professional to determine the factors associated with continued care. Insurance companies, Medicaid/Medicare, and other funding sources may have rules associated with what constitutes termination. Additionally, in the initial phases of counseling, the counseling professional should discuss what factors are associated with termination of treatment. These may include the accomplishment of treatment goals or the lack of accomplishment of treatment goals.

Disability Considerations

A disability is defined as "having a mental or physical impairment (difference) that substantially limits one or more major life activities (e.g., eating, driving, working), having a record of such an impairment or being regarded of having such an impairment" and may include physical, psychiatric, cognitive, psychological, and emotional disabilities (Upton & Harper, 2002). It is estimated that approximately 56.7 million people in the United States (U.S.) [19% of the population] have a disability (U.S. Census Bureau, 2012). As noted by Sprong, Upton, and Pappas (2012), substance use disorders [i.e., abuse or dependence] occur two to four times more often among persons with disabilities in comparison to the general population (Koch, Nelipovich, & Sneed, 2002; Sprong et al., 2012). The Substance Abuse Mental Health Services Administration (SAMHSA) suggested that approximately 4.7 million Americans with disabilities experience coexisting substance use disorders and physical or mental disabilities (Office on Disability, 2010), and approximately 22.3 million individuals in the United States aged 12 or older (9% of general population) met DSM-IV TR diagnostic criteria for substance abuse or dependence in 2007 (Walls, Moore, Batiste, & Loy, 2009). Disability is another essential consideration that needs to be addressed within a treatment plan, as it will likely have an impact on the individual's life in addition to the substance use.

West (2007) assessed the accessibility of substance abuse treatment facilities in the United States for people with disabilities and found that most facilities in their sample self-reported a variety of barriers to physical accessibility and the lack of services and physical accommodations. A counseling professional specializing in drug/alcohol treatment may not be aware of the other issues associated with disability that might need to be addressed within treatment, as curriculum within drug/alcohol treatment programs might not completely cover psychosocial and medical aspects of disability (with the exception of Rehabilitation Counseling programs). Additionally, the most effective treatment planning occurs when a rapport is established between the counseling professional and client. SAMHSA's (2009b) Treatment Improvement Protocol (TIP) 29 provides some examples of disability etiquette to prevent from offending or being disrespectful to clients with disabilities:

1. Ask a client who has a disability if there are any accommodations that he or she may need for successful treatment.
2. Use people-first language when referring to people with disabilities.
3. A service animal should not be distracted from its job (the animal should not be touched or petted).
4. Look directly at a person who is deaf when communicating, so lip-reading and facial expressions can be communicated.
5. Touching the client's wheelchair may be offensive to the individual (e.g., leaning on the chair).

Although there are numerous disability categories, we will provide examples of special considerations when developing a treatment plan when the client has either (a) brain injury (BI) and/or a (b) spinal cord injury. It is estimated that 50% of people with traumatic brain injuries and spinal cord injuries use substances (SAMHSA, 2011). Therefore, special consideration must be given when developing a comprehensive treatment plan. For example, below are some specific examples that could be incorporated into substance abuse treatment (Corrigan & Lamb-Hart, 2004; DeLambo, Chandras, Homa, & Chandras, 2009) provided there are special considerations when working with people with coexisting disabilities (as cited in: https://www.counseling.org/Resources/Library/VISTAS/2009-V-Online/DeLambo-Chandras-Homa-Chandras2.pdf):

1. Modify admission criteria: Remove abstinence from prescription medications (e.g., Valium) as a program requirement.
2. Determine unique learning strategies: Avoid jargon; use concrete written materials and allow tape recording. Give extra time for work, paraphrase and repeat.
3. Determine unique communication styles: Ask how client reads and writes or evaluate samples.
4. Avoid many environmental stimuli: Minimize distractions.
5. Be aware of attention span deficits.
6. Give breaks to combat fatigue.
7. Address inappropriate social behaviors in a gentle manner: Don't assume the individual knows right from wrong.
8. Redirect excessive speech.
9. Be cautious when inferring client motivation levels: Do not assume that noncompliance arises from lack of motivation or resistance.
10. Don't assume a missed appointment is intentional or due to resistance: Punctuality can be due to time management, poor memory, and transportation issues.

From "Traumatic Brain Injuries and Substance Abuse: Implications for Rehabilitation Professionals," *VISTAS Online* by D.A. DeLambo, K. V. Chandras, D. Homa, & V. Chandras. Copyright © 2009 by American Counseling Association. Reprinted by permission.

11. The single most important factor for successful treatment is the therapeutic alliance between counselor and client: Utilize a proven approach (e.g., Rogerian) that builds this partnership.
12. Enlist the client's social circle (family, friends, and service providers) to reinforce goals.
13. Don't assume that learning will be generalized to other environments.
14. Be delicate and caring during confrontation.
15. Repeat instructions and strategies: Repeat, review, rehearse.
16. Attend to transportation issues: These are often a major treatment barrier.
17. Increase treatment compliance/attendance through incentives: These can be financial, as well as reminder phone calls and related strategies.

Thus, a counseling professional should consider the above information when working with a client who also has a disability.

Brain Injury

A BI usually results from a violent blow to or a jolt of the head, or from an object (e.g., bullet) penetrating the skull (Falvo & Holland, 2018). The structure of the brain, skull, and surrounding tissues makes the brain quite susceptible to injury as a result of blows to or jolts of the head. The intensity does not have to be extreme to cause a BI and small amount of pressure, force, frequency wave, or locations of contact can create conditions in which the skull and cerebrospinal fluid cannot effectively protect the brain from damage. For example, during a car crash, the car comes to an abrupt stop, but a rider's body will still have strong forward momentum. A rapid stop or contact with an external object may cause the brain to move back and forth inside the skull and make contact with the internal surfaces; this is termed a coup-countercoup injury (Young et al., 2015).

BIs occur very often in the United States. For example, according to the National Highway Traffic Safety Administration (2015), there is a motor vehicle accident every 60 seconds. In 2015, these accidents resulted in 2.44 million injuries, with 14.3% resulting in a BI. The prevalence of BI is ever-increasing due to the numerous ways in which traffic accidents occur, including by way of traffic accidents, falls, gun shots, and improvised explosive devices (IED) to name a few. It is estimated that in the United States, 1.7 million people sustain a BI each year. Of this number, approximately 52,000 results in death, 275,000 are hospitalized, and 1.365 million are treated and released from hospital emergency rooms. The leading causes of BI among the general population include falls (35.2%), motor vehicle accidents (17.3%), being struck by/against events (colliding with a moving or stationary object: 16.5%), assaults (10%), and unknown/other (21%).

The relationship between *BI* and substance abuse was explored as early as 1987 by the Brain Injury Association of America [formerly known as the National Head Injury Foundation] (Sparadeo, Strauss, & Barth, 1990). At the time, there were limited resources available to assist healthcare professionals and counseling professionals to treat individuals with these coexisting disabilities (i.e., BI and substance-related disorders). More recently, it is estimated that 12% of people who are 16 and older who went to rehabilitation treatment for BI were also using illicit drugs in the months prior to their injury and 23% for alcohol abuse (Cuthbert et al., 2015). The screening, brief intervention, and referral to treatment (SBIRT) model is sometimes used to assess whether a person with a BI may have substance-related barriers that would require additional treatment from a counseling professional (Nilsen et al., 2008). Once substance abuse is detected for the client with a BI, the professional will use motivational interviewing techniques (e.g., scaling) to guide a discussion toward substance use treatment (Holloway, 2012). This step is usually performed in a primary care and emergency setting for individuals with mild to moderate BI. It has yet to be used for people with severe BI due to cognitive and expressive deficits.

If a client with a BI has been referred for substance use treatment, the counseling professional should work with the client's BI rehabilitation team to ascertain what accommodations might be required for the client to successfully complete treatment. For example, the most common symptoms associated with

BI include confusion, disorientation, loss of memory, headaches, dizziness, nausea, visual degradation, irritability, passing out, vertigo, poor coordination, and loss of balance (Falvo & Holland, 2018). Clients with moderate brain injuries may experience the same symptoms aforementioned but may also experience paralysis (e.g., leg function may not be present), seizures, limited control related to bowel/bladder, ability to regulate body temperature, hormonal changes, perseveration, impulsiveness, language processing deficiencies, executive function limitations, aphasia (i.e., expressive and receptive), slurred speech, partial or total loss of vision, partial or total hearing loss, denial or lack of awareness, and increased psychological symptoms (e.g., depression). We recommend an integrated approach where the counseling professional within the substance-related treatment program collaborate with the BI treatment team. Some questions that might assist the counseling professional in identifying other barriers include:

- *Pre-injury life/habits*: What was the client's life like prior to obtaining the BI?
- *Post-injury life/habits*: What is client's life like now?
- *Rehabilitation process*: Where is the client currently in their rehabilitation process for the BI?
- *Adjustment*: How is the client adjusting to having a BI?
- *Classification of BI*: Does the client have a mild, moderate, or severe BI?
- *Support*: Does the client have a strong support team (e.g., family, friends) in place?
- *Activities of Daily Living (ADLs)*: Does the client have caregivers and support?
- *Architectural Barriers*: Identify and modify any physical barriers to treatment.
- *Cognitive Challenges:* Does the client have challenges with his or her long-term, short-term, and working memory?
- *Secondary Challenges:* Does the client have secondary challenges (such as vision, hearing, dizziness, headache) that need to be considered when making a treatment plan?
- *Expressive Challenges:* Does the client have struggles with communicating
- *Medication:* Are the medications causing any challenges or side effects that affect their daily lives?

Spinal Cord Injury

A spinal cord injury is the result of damage to any part of the spinal cord or nerves at the end of the spinal canal and often causes permanent changes in strength, sensation, and other body functions below the level of the injury (Falvo & Holland, 2018). If a client has a complete spinal cord injury, all of the feeling (sensory) and the ability to control movement is lost below the level of injury. Whereas, an incomplete spinal cord injury would still allow for some motor or sensory function below the level of the injury. A client who has paraplegia will have paralysis in part or all of the trunk, legs, and pelvic organs. Tetraplegia (quadriplegia) is when the arms, hands, trunk, legs, and pelvic organs are affected by the spinal cord injury.

Research has shown that people who acquire a spinal cord injury have suicide rates approximately three times higher than the general population during the first 12 years (Yue, Massaro, Krause, Chen, & Devivo, 2014), and significant depression may require pharmacological intervention (Saulino, 2014). Oftentimes, people with spinal cord injuries will use drugs and/or alcohol to cope with the newly acquired disability. Alcohol can increase skin breakdown through dehydration or forgetting to shift positions. Additionally, the client may forget to catheterize, which can increase the change of having a bladder infection or urinary tract infection. Previous research has shown that having a spinal cord injury reduces the likelihood of having a successful substance abuse recovery (DeLambo et al., 2009). Furthermore, a potential factor influencing successful substance abuse recovery is that people with spinal cord injuries are significantly underemployed or unemployed, and this leads to a greater chance of relapse. Melvin, Davis, and Koch (2012) found that employment is a strong predictor of substance abuse treatment, and yet research (e.g., West, 2008) has found that only 31% of substance abuse treatment facilities in the United States prioritize employment by offering a vocational counseling component. Coviello, Zanis, Wesnoski, and Domis (2009) found that incorporating vocational counseling within treatment not only led to a reduction in drug use but also to a reduction in crime rates and risky behavior. Therefore, a collaborative approach between a counseling professional and a vocational rehabilitation counselor would be helpful in meeting the employment needs of clients with disabilities. In addition to employment-related obstacles, a counseling professional should also consider the following:

- *Pre-injury life/habits*: What was the client's life like prior to obtaining the spinal cord injury?
- *Post-injury life/habits*: What is the client's life like now?
- *Rehabilitation process*: Is the client required to attend post-acute care for continued treatment of the spinal cord injury?
- *Adjustment*: How is the client adjusting to the spinal cord injury?
- *Support*: What support systems are in place for the client?
- *Activities of Daily Living (ADLs)*: Does the client require the use of caregivers to provide support for ADLs?
- *Architectural Barriers*: Identify and modify any physical barriers to treatment such as inaccessible restrooms, parking, doorways.
- *Medication:* What impact will medication have in terms of side effects?
- *Reminder*: The client may have a longer rehabilitation process.
- *Services*: The client may need flexibility with breaks to relieve pressure from sitting in a wheelchair.

Case Scenario

Sheila is a 17-year-old, white female, who currently lives with her mother and younger brother and sister. Sheila started using marijuana at an early age, and eventually she progressed to the use of heroin. Sheila currently reports that she uses it twice daily and reports having tolerance symptoms and experiences withdrawal symptoms such as headaches when not using. She reports that she is not addicted and is capable of quitting at any time. Recently, she was involved in illegal activities (residential burglary), was arrested, and forced to detoxify in the local county jail. As part of her court hearing, she was offered prison for 2–3 years or to enter a 6-month inpatient substance abuse treatment program. She chose the drug rehabilitation program and was admitted into treatment after spending 25 days in the county jail. Sheila reported that she does not want to be in treatment but would rather be in treatment than jail.

Sheila's parents separated at the age of 15 after her father had an affair with another woman, who is now his current wife. Sheila reports that her father has been an active part of her life when it is convenient for him. She feels that her father left her and his family for another woman and suggests that her father does not make attempts to be involved in her life, except when he needs help with his business (restaurant owner). Sheila has opened up about her problems within her family and how it has impacted her drug use. She says her mom has been consulting with her about her own personal problems and Sheila feels that since she is the oldest child, she needs to listen to her mother's issues. Sheila stated that her mother has recently found a boyfriend. However, the boyfriend uses heroin and other drugs.

Sheila reported that she continues to have relationship issues with her father. Furthermore, Sheila stated that her father only views her as a business opportunity, not as a child. While in jail, Sheila's father did not visit her, and while in treatment, Sheila has only spoken with her father a few times on the phone for approximately 20 minutes each time. Sheila mentioned that usually her father will want to hang up after he is finished talking about things going on in his life. Sheila claimed that she never is able to talk about her issues and wants to tell her father but feels uncomfortable doing so. Sheila wants to ask her father questions related to the divorce and why he left for a new family but doesn't want to make the relationship any worse.

Sheila stated that she has a boyfriend named Mickey, who does not engage in drug usage. Mickey is usually present when Sheila uses heroin with her friends, because he is afraid that she will overdose. Sheila reported that she loves Mickey very much and would like to get married at some point in their lives. She enjoys writing, reading, and listening to music. She was awarded a scholarship for her writing during her junior year of high school. She reported she was kicked out of school for never attending but would like to go to college one day. Sheila reported that her father mentioned several years ago that he wanted her to take over the family business, but this was before he had children with his new wife. Sheila has obtained enough credit hours to be at the sophomore level of high school. She is afraid that if she returns, she will be judged negatively for being behind. She stated she would like to attend college for journalism or creative writing if she ever graduates.

Discussion Questions

1. What are some potential challenges that Sheila faces?

2. What stage of change do you feel that Sheila would be in and why?

3. The scenario states that Sheila was mandated to inpatient treatment. Is this the most appropriate level of care for Sheila? Please provide rationale to support your response.

4. What are some potential goals, objectives, and action plans that the client may have?

5. What other treatments would you recommend for Sheila?

Homework Activity

Movie/Television Series Character Treatment Plan Assignment

Directions:

1. Select a movie or a television series where a main character presents an issue with drugs and/or alcohol.
2. Write a paragraph not less than 250 words about how this movie/television series is personally meaningful to you. Describe the interaction of your chosen character with the other characters. What did you like or dislike about the character? How might your dislikes impact the counseling relationships? Any other observations, patterns, or connections that you think are important to document?
3. Compare the individual to topics discussed throughout this textbook. Does the character meet criteria for substance-related disorders? What behavior is the character displaying that would lead you to this conclusion? Are there any cultural dimensions that should be considered in a treatment plan? Would you use any psychological testing and if so, why would this be beneficial? What are some counseling theories that might be useful when working with this client? What are the primary issues you notice related to the character that might be an obstacle during the treatment recovery process?

Counseling Treatment Plan:

1. Write the counseling treatment plan for the character you have chosen. The treatment plan should consist of 2–3 long-term goals, 2–3 short-term goals/objectives for each long-term goal, and not less than 6 specific treatment-goal-targeted interventions/action steps.

   a. The character I chose as a hypothetical client is:

      Name of Client:
      Name of Movie:

   b. **Presenting Problems:** The movie indicated that this character may have the following clinical issues. These will include any problems or barriers that the character may have. Are there any patterns that the character is displaying that could become problematic?

      Problem #1:
      Problem #2:
      Problem #3:
      Problem #4:

   c. **Treatment Goals:** Oftentimes, once there are several problems identified, treatment goals would be developed to reduce or eliminate these problems. For example, Bryan had difficulty maintaining employment, which he described as being a contributing factor to him using alcohol (cope with lack of stable employment). A treatment goal was developed to reduce this barrier. If I were treating this character as a professional counselor, I would include the following treatment goals in my plan.

   d. **Treatment Interventions:** In order to meet these treatment goals, I would provide the specific, time-limited, observable, logical, and targeted treatment interventions. Remember, we are using the S.M.A.R.T. framework to write our treatment goals. Below is an example of how the treatment goals can be written with the short-term objectives and action steps.

      Long-term Goal #1:
         Short-term objective#1:
            Intervention/Action Step 1:
            Intervention/Action Step 2:
            Intervention/Action Step 3:
            Intervention/Action Step 4:
            Intervention/Action Step 5:
            Intervention/Action Step 6:
         Short-term objective#2:
            Intervention/Action Step 1:
            Intervention/Action Step 2:
            Intervention/Action Step 3:
            Intervention/Action Step 4:
            Intervention/Action Step 5:
            Intervention/Action Step 6:

References

Bovend'Eerdt, T. J. H., Botell, R. E., & Wade, D. T. (2009). Writing SMART rehabilitation goals and achieving goal attainment scaling: A practical guide. *Clinical Rehabilitation, 23*(4), 352–361.

Cao, Y., J. S. Krause, and N. D. DiPiro. (2014). Unmet expectations of adjustment and depressive symptoms among people with traumatic spinal cord injury. *Rehabilitation Psychology, 59*, 313–320.

Commission on Accreditation of Rehabilitation Facility (CARF). (2018). *Behavioral health.* Tucson, AZ: Author.

Corrigan, J. D., & Lamb-Hart, G. L. (2004). *Substance abuse issues after traumatic brain injury: Living with brain injury.* Vienna, VA: Brain Injury Association of America.

Coviello, D. M., Zanis, D. A., Wesnoski, S. A., & Domis, S. W. (2009). An integrated drug counseling and employment intervention for methadone clients. *Journal of Psychoactive Drugs, 41*(2), 189–197.

Cuthbert, J. P., Harrison-Felix, C., Corrigan, J. D., Kreider, S., Bell, J. M., Coronado, V. G., & Whiteneck, G. G. (2015). Epidemiology of adults receiving acute inpatient rehabilitation for a primary diagnosis of traumatic brain injury in the United States. *Journal of Head Trauma Rehabilitation, 30*(2), 122–135. doi:10.1097/HTR.0000000000000012.

DeLambo, D. A., Chandras, K. V., Homa, D., & Chandras, S. V. (2009). Traumatic brain injuries and substance abuse: Implications for rehabilitation professionals. *American Counseling Association.* Retrieved from https://www.counseling.org/Resources/Library/VISTAS/2009-V-Online/DeLambo-Chandras-Homa-Chandras2.pdf

DeLambo, D. A., Chandras, K. V., Homa, D., & Chandras, S. V. (2010). Spinal cord injury and substance abuse: Implications for rehabilitation professionals. Retrieved from http://counselingoutfitters.com/vistas/vistas10/Article_83.pdf

Donsel, A. V. (2014). Residential substance abuse treatment: Impact of concurrent utilization review. Report to The Vermont Legislature. Retrieved from https://legislature.vermont.gov/assets/Legislative-Reports/SA-res-care-days12.12.14.pdf

Eells, T. D. (2015). *Psychotherapy case formulation.* Washington, DC: American Psychological Association.

Falvo, D. R., & Holland, B. E. (2018). *Medical and psychosocial aspects of chronic illness and disability* (6th ed.). Sudbury, MA: Jones and Bartlett Publishers.

Gilmore, G. W., Seirup, H., & Rubinstein, R. (2011). The spectrum of treatment options & their components. In J. Stano (Ed.). *Substance abuse: Treatment and rehabilitation.* Osage Beech, MO: Aspen Professional Services.

Holloway, M. (2012). Motivational interviewing and acquired brain injury. *Social Care and Neurodisability, 3*(3), 122–130.

Koch, D. S., Nelipovich, M., & Sneed, Z. (2002). Alcohol and other drug abuse as coexisting disabilities: Implications for counselors serving persons who are blind or visually impaired. *RE-View, 33*(4), 151–159.

Mee-Lee, D. (2013). The ASAM criteria: Treatment criteria for addictive, substance-related, and co-occurring conditions (3rd ed.). Retrieved from https://www.asam.org/resources/the-asam-criteria/about

Melvin, A., Davis, S., & Koch, D. S. (2012). Employment as a predictor of substance abuse treatment completion. *Journal of Rehabilitation, 78*, 31–37.

National Highway Traffic Safety Administration. (2015). Advancing safety on America's roads. Retrieved from https://one.nhtsa.gov/nhtsa/accomplishments/2015/index.html

Nilsen, P., Baird, J., Mello, M. J., Nirenberg, T., Woolard, R., Bendtsen, P., & Longabaugh, R. (2008). A systematic review of emergency care brief alcohol interventions for injury patients. *Journal of Substance Abuse Treatment, 35*(2), 184–201.

Office on Disability: U.S. Department of Health and Human Services. (2010). Substance abuse and disability.

Saulino, M. (2014). Spinal cord injury pain. *Physical Medicine and Rehabilitation Clinics of North America, 25*(2), 397–410.

Schuckit, M. A. (1994). The treatment of stimulant dependence. *Addiction, 89,* 1559–1563.

Sommers-Flanagan, J., & Sommers-Flanagan, R. (2015). *Clinical interviewing* (5th ed.). Hoboken, NJ: Wiley & Sons.

Sparadeo, F. R., Strauss, D., & Barth, J. T. (1990). The incidence, impact, and treatment of substance abuse in head trauma rehabilitation. *The Journal of Head Trauma Rehabilitation, 5*(3), 1–8.

Sprong, M. E., Upton, T. D., & Pappas, M. (2012). Utilization of community rehabilitation programs: Screening for alcohol and drugs. *Journal of Rehabilitation, 78*(2), 13–19.

Substance Abuse Mental Health Services Administration [SAMHSA]. (2009a). Chapter 5: Treatment engagement, placement, and planning. In Substance Abuse Treatment: Addressing the Specific Needs of Women. Treatment Improvement Protocol (TIP) Series, No. 51. Retrieved from https://www.ncbi.nlm.nih.gov/books/NBK83238/

Substance Abuse Mental Health Services Administration [SAMHSA]. (2009b). Substance use disorder treatment for people with physical and cognitive disabilities. Treatment Improvement Protocol (TIP) Series, No. 29. Retrieved from https://www.ncbi.nlm.nih.gov/books/NBK83238/

Substance Abuse and Mental Health Services Administration: Office of Applied Studies: U.S. Department of Health and Human Services. (2011). Substance abuse and disability. Retrieved from http://www.hhs.gov/od/about/fact_sheets/substanceabuse.html

United States Census Bureau. (2012). Nearly 1 in 5 people have a disability in the U.S. Retrieved from https://www.census.gov/newsroom/releases/archives/miscellaneous/cb12-134.html

Upton, T. D., & Harper, D. C. (2002). Multidimensional disability attitudes and equitable evaluation of educational accommodations by college students without disabilities. *Journal of Postsecondary Education and Disability, 15*(2), 115–130.

Walls, R. T., Moore, L. C., Batiste, L. C., & Loy, B. (2009). Vocational rehabilitation and job accommodations for individuals with substance abuse disorders. *Journal of Rehabilitation, 75*(4), 35–44.

West, S. L. (2007). The accessibility of substance abuse treatment facilities in the United States for persons with disabilities. *Journal of Substance Abuse Treatment, 33*(1), 1–5.

West, S. L. (2008). The utilization of vocational rehabilitation services in substance abuse treatment facilities in the U.S. *Journal of Vocational Rehabilitation, 29,* 71–75.

Young, L., Rule, G. T., Bocchieri, R. T., Walilko, T. J., Burns, J. M., & Ling, G. (2015). When physics meets biology: Low and high-velocity penetration, blunt impact, and blast injuries to the brain. *Frontiers in Neurology, 6,* 89. doi:10.3389/fneur.2015.00089

Yue, C., Massaro, J. F., Krause, J. S., Chen, Y., & Devivo, M. J. (2014). Suicide mortality after spinal cord injury in the United States: Injury cohort analysis. *Physical Medicine and Rehabilitation, 95*(2), 230–235.

Printed in the USA
CPSIA information can be obtained
at www.ICGtesting.com
LVHW010405311023
762565LV00012B/1284

9 781524 959753